24 Hr Day

A Cancer Survivor's Raw Journey into Healing, Hope, and Human Potential

BOB CAIN

24HRDAY

A CANCER SURVIVOR'S RAW JOURNEY INTO HEALING, HOPE AND HUMAN POTENTIAL

BOB CAIN

24HrDay
PRESS

Copyright © 2025 24HrDay Press

All rights reserved. Written by Bob Cain.

No part of this book may be reproduced, stored in a retrieval system, or transmitted by any means—electronic, mechanical, photocopying, recording, or otherwise—without prior written permission from the author, except in the case of brief quotations embodied in critical articles or reviews.

First Edition

ISBN: 978-1-0696770-1-3

Cover Design: Lauren Cain

Interior Layout: Bob Cain

Editors: D'Arcy Saunders, Nancy Cain, Kristie Robertson, Amy Baker, Wendy Thompson

Foreword by: Randy Robles

Printed in Canada

Published by 24HrDay Press

This is a work of non-fiction. The events and reflections described are based on the author's lived experience. Certain names may have been changed to protect privacy.

 Formatted with Vellum

COPYRIGHT NOTICE & DISCLAIMER

Throughout *24HrDay*, select quotes, lyrics, and excerpts from beloved songs, films, and written works are included to enrich the emotional texture of the story and pay tribute to the voices that helped guide me through.

These quoted materials are used with deep respect and under the principles of fair use—for purposes of commentary, reflection, education, and artistic transformation. All original rights remain with the respective creators and copyright holders.

If you are a rights holder and believe something has been used in error, please reach out directly. This book was created in the spirit of gratitude, reverence, and healing.

The content in this book is intended for informational and inspirational purposes only and reflects the personal experiences and opinions of the author. It is **not medical advice** and should not be treated as such. Readers should always consult with qualified healthcare professionals regarding any questions or decisions related to their health, treatment, or medical care.

THIS BOOK IS DEDICATED TO:

D'Arcy Saunders — *Your unwavering support has been my anchor throughout this journey. You show up for me in every moment, and I will never stop being grateful for your love.*

My family — *To my parents, Brian and Nancy Cain, for a lifetime of love and encouragement.
To my children and grandchildren: Aidan and Linda, Niall and Lauren, Oliver and Noah — you are my greatest source of pride and purpose.*

My friends — *To the many amazing friends who kept me laughing and uplifted during the most difficult times. Your encouragement is a lifeline. Your support carried me through.*

Dr. Andrea MacNeill, Surgical Oncologist — *Through your rare blend of vision, expertise, and deep humanity, you offered me not just a path to healing, but the gift of more life. Your presence and work ripple outward in ways beyond measure. Thank you, from the bottom of my heart.*

The medical teams Vancouver General Hospital (VGH - T8, T9) and BC Cancer, Surrey—*Your skill, compassion, and relentless dedication saved my life.*

FOREWORD

Dear Reader,

You are about to learn about my friend Bob Cain. He is an energetic, vivacious, kind, and friendly person — the life of the party and the one you sit down with if you ever need an empathetic ear.

We grew up in the same blue-collar town in southern Ontario called St. Catharines. In our young adult years, Bob was a ball of energy — a person who thrived in social settings. He was (and still is) the guy who whipped out his acoustic guitar whenever there was a gathering around a fire pit. A natural-born entertainer, philosopher, poet, and adventurer. One of the funniest people you could ever meet, and one of the best conversationalists you could ever share time with.

When I was 25, I left town to work in the United States. Over time — especially when distance is a factor — you tend to lose touch with people. I generally lost touch with Bob over the following ten years or so.

However, out of the blue, business brought Bob to New York City. I was living nearby, in Hoboken, New Jersey at the time. It turned out that Bob needed to stay in New York for a while, so I offered him my extra bedroom in my two-bedroom condo for as long as he wanted to stay.

He took me up on my offer and ended up spending about two months with me in the summer of 2007. It was one of the best summers of my life as we went out five nights a week, drinking beer, listening to and playing music, and chasing women. For a brief moment, it was like we were young adults again back in St. Catharines.

Eventually, Bob returned home and then shortly afterward moved out west to British Columbia, where he still lives today. Despite the distance, we never lost touch this time around.

I was one of the first friends that Bob called after he got a terrifying cancer diagnosis out of the blue in 2024 at age 52. I am not a religious person, but I felt that a higher power was talking through me and directly to Bob in that phone call. Having known Bob for over 30 years, I felt that if anybody could defeat cancer, it was him — and not only that, but he would have the strength and caring to share his victory with the world.

So instead of sulking or playing the victim, Bob decided to meet this challenge head-on, and to perceive this obstacle as a chance of a lifetime. A gift instead of a disaster.

Bob, with his brutal honesty, will be bringing you along for the ride in this book. He chronicles every step and lets you behind the curtain of his doctor's office visits and his surgeries. In the pages that follow, not only does Bob provide the framework for tackling cancer with the best possible frame of mind — he also teaches us that every hour of every day is a gift. Through this book,

I hope you get to know Bob as well as I do.

Enjoy the ride!
—Randy Robles

INTRODUCTION

On January 27, 2024, I received a life-changing diagnosis: stage 4 colon cancer that had spread throughout my abdomen. That moment became a turning point—a call to fight for my life and, in the process, transform into a better version of myself.

This book chronicles my 16-month cancer journey from diagnosis to treatment and recovery. I endured 24 weeks of intensive chemotherapy, followed by major abdominal surgery to save my life. There were many battles along the way. Through them, I learned invaluable lessons about time, relationships, mental resilience, and the preciousness of life itself.

I discovered that every day matters. With only 24 hours in each day, I began to notice and cherish the little moments more deeply. I became determined to make the most of each one. That realization changed how I approached both cancer and life. I emerged stronger, fitter, and, perhaps, a little wiser. I found a renewed connection to this world, to the people in it, and to those I cherish most.

This experience prompted a profound shift in my mindset—one I came to call the "24HrDay" strategy. It's a health and wellness methodology rooted in living fully, one day at a time. I fought through aggressive chemotherapy, laparoscopic surgery, and a complex 14-hour Cytoreductive/ HIPEC surgery. Each phase carried its own risks and demanded everything I had.

Throughout the journey, I was fortunate to receive exceptional medical care in Canada, and I'm deeply grateful for the healthcare professionals whose support helped carry me through.

As I reflected, I realized my cancer diagnosis had become a catalyst for personal growth. It wasn't a threat—it was an opportunity. In hindsight, I believe it arrived precisely when I needed it. It woke me up.

I began to prioritize my connections with family and friends. I became more present and more intentional in how I lived. I embraced each day with as much strength as I could muster and encouraged others to do the same.

My goal in sharing this story is not just to describe a medical journey, but to tell a story of transformation. By reframing cancer as a teacher instead of a curse, I survived it—with a clean bill of health and a fresh lease on life at 53.

I hope this book inspires you to embrace each and every 24HrDay.

Nietzsche was the one who did the job for me. At a certain moment in his life, the idea came to him of what he called 'the love of your fate.' Whatever your fate is, whatever the hell happens, you say, 'This is what I need.' It may look like a wreck, but go at it as though it were an opportunity, a challenge. If you bring love to that moment--not discouragement--you will find the strength is there. Any disaster you can survive is an improvement in your character, your stature, and your life. What a privilege! This is when the spontaneity of your own nature will have a chance to flow.

Then, when looking back at your life, you will see that the moments which seemed to be great failures followed by wreckage were the incidents that shaped the life you have now. You'll see that this is really true. Nothing can happen to you that is not positive. Even though it looks and feels at the moment like a negative crisis, it is not. The crisis throws you back, and when you are required to exhibit strength, it comes. ~Joseph Campbell

Joseph Campbell Wisdom A quote Randy Robles sent me at just the right time. It landed like a spark, illuminating a path through darkness. From that moment forward, this idea became the foundation of my mental framework—and ultimately the core philosophy behind 24HrDay.

PROLOGUE

Each day is a gift, and we should strive to make the most of it for as long as our physical and mental health allow. This realization became the cornerstone of my mindset during my battle with cancer in 2024.

In January, I received my diagnosis. By February, I learned that my treatment plan would include 24 weeks of chemotherapy and major abdominal surgery, followed by a 3–6 month recovery. The prospect of a long and gruelling year loomed, and I had a lot to process. My mother offered me a piece of advice: **"Well, Bob, how do you eat an elephant? One bite at a time."** This simple analogy resonated deeply. I knew I needed to approach this journey one day at a time.

One of the most important things I did was place complete trust in modern Western medicine. With an honours degree in Neuroscience, I understood the scientific method and the rigorous research, clinical trials, and evidence required for any treatment to be approved. That background gave me confidence in the process I was about to undergo.

The first obvious step was to fully commit to the guidance of my surgeon and medical oncologist. It was a no-brainer—I trusted their training and experience completely. My job was to show up, follow instructions, and give everything I had to my end of the deal.

By embracing this mindset, I formed a collaborative relationship with my medical team. I knew they were doing everything in their power to help me survive. My role was to match their effort with discipline, positivity, and presence.

Adopting the "Carpe Diem" Philosophy

I began to fine-tune my understanding of living in the moment. My daily focus became simple: give my best effort, and stay aligned with what mattered. I started tracking habits across all areas of life: fitness, diet, hygiene, home care, and relationships. I set daily, weekly, and monthly goals. If I executed the plan, I believed I could win.

Instead of being overwhelmed, I broke things into manageable chunks. I disciplined my thoughts, choosing to shut down negativity with a phrase that became a mantra:

"It's not happening today."

By managing the moment, I could stay in the fight.

This book is a full account of what followed: my diagnosis, the 24 weeks of chemotherapy, the 14-hour Cytoreductive/HIPEC surgery, and the six-month recovery that brought me back to life. It includes over 80 appointments during a 16-month stretch. My goal is to be transparent, honest, and thorough in telling the story.

Treatment Summary (January 2024 – May 2025)

Surgeries (4 total):
- IV Port Implant
- Investigative Laparoscopy
- Cytoreductive/HIPEC Surgery
- IV Port Removal

Imaging (8 total):
- CT Scans (6)
- PET Scan (1)
- Ultrasound (1)

Chemotherapy:
- 12 cycles, ~52 hours per cycle

Bloodwork:
- 18 appointments

Consultations:
- 18 appointments

Wound Care:
- 10 sessions

Hospitalization:
- 8 nights (post-surgery and recovery)

The **Canadian healthcare system** covered nearly 100% of my treatment costs. My only expenses were travel, medications not fully covered, and basic incidentals—roughly $500 in total.

Parking for Surrey Memorial appointments was covered, and BC Cancer reimbursed all costs for my PET scan in Kelowna, including travel and accommodation.

I believe I received world-class care that saved my life—essentially for the price of a few groceries. The **Canada Pension Plan** also provided a $1,500/month disability benefit during the seven months I was unable to work. I had no insurance coverage at the time—no disability, life, or medical. That benefit was my only source of income.

I am profoundly grateful to the Canadian government, to BC Cancer, and to every healthcare professional who supported me through this fight.

Preview of Appendix B: Interview with Dr. MacNeill

Six months after surgery, I interviewed **Dr. Andrea MacNeill**, one of the two surgeons who performed my Cytoreductive/HIPEC procedure. The full transcript is in *Appendix B*, but key highlights are summarized below to offer context on the complexity of my treatment.

Dr. MacNeill is a surgical oncologist at VGH and BC Cancer, and a clinical associate professor at UBC. She specializes in sarcoma and peritoneal malignancies and is a pioneer in **planetary health**, creating healthcare systems that support both human and environmental well-being.

KEY POINTS FROM THE INTERVIEW:

- **Cytoreductive surgery** aims to remove *all visible cancer* in the abdomen, sometimes involving multiple organs.

- **HIPEC** (Hyperthermic Intraperitoneal Chemotherapy) follows the cytoreductive surgery with a heated chemo rinse to kill remaining microscopic cancer cells.
- Before the advent of HIPEC, **metastatic peritoneal cancer was considered terminal** within 12 months.
- **HIPEC and cytoreduction** were developed in the 1990s and have drastically improved survival outcomes —from 5% to over 50%.
- My own surgery involved removal of the **right colon, omentum, diaphragm lining, flanks**, and **portions of the rectum and small intestine**.
- Recovery is challenging. Major complications occur in 15–30% of patients, and fatigue can last 3–6 months or more.

Bob and Dr. Andrea MacNeill (April 28, 2025)

This is the story of what it's like to go through that.
A story of illness and survival.
Of grief and grace.
Of pain, precision, and personal transformation.

LET'S BEGIN.

CHAPTER 1

FOUNDATIONS

> *"My life has been extraordinary, blessed and cursed, and won."*
> — Smashing Pumpkins, *"Muzzle"*

BEFORE WE BEGIN

To truly understand the 24HrDay mindset, you first need to know the person behind it. This opening chapter isn't a memoir—it's an invitation. A quick journey through the pivotal chapters of my life that shaped how I think, how I fight, and how I choose to live. By getting to know where I come from—my values, my struggles, my turning points—you'll better understand how I came to build a system for taking radical control in the face of crisis. It's not about the past for nostalgia's sake. It's about context for what comes next.

. . .

The Analog Childhood

I was born on April 4, 1972, in St. Catharines, Ontario, where I spent the first 41 years of my life. My childhood was fortunate, nurtured by two loving and supportive parents. Growing up in the 70s and 80s, life was beautifully analog: outdoor play, sports, BMX bikes, pop culture, and just enough mischief to keep it interesting.

We lived on Grantham Avenue in a neighbourhood where everyone knew each other. We played hide-and-seek until the streetlights came on and hosted backyard hockey games on our homemade rink. Halloween was a full-production event, with my parents handing out candy while packs of kids roamed the neighbourhood, pumped full of sugar and adrenaline. I was a high-energy kid who hated boredom, always looking for something to build, break, or explore. There was a constant pulse of possibility.

My earliest memory is my first day of kindergarten at Carleton Public School. That morning, my mom handed me a brand-new pair of purple Cheetah running shoes. I stared at them in the backseat, convinced they had superpowers. As we arrived, I spotted the kindergarten doors about 80 meters away and just took off. I sprinted across the lawn like it was an Olympic trial. The shoes were fast. I had arrived.

The Non-Negotiable: Freedom

I was generally well-behaved but hated losing my freedom. Getting grounded was the worst punishment imaginable. Once, I even begged my mom to spank me instead of grounding me in my room for a week. I still remember watching my friends play outside while I sat by the window, seething. Looking back, that was the first real sign that freedom would always be non-negotiable for me. That instinct—to fight for autonomy—would echo through every major decision I made from that point forward.

The Friday Escape Clause

My academic performance in elementary school was decent—I coasted, content to stay comfortably in the middle of the pack. I wasn't the best student, but I paid attention, mostly. I got by on charm and curiosity. Everything changed in grade eight when the principal told my parents he believed I was capable of more and recommended I join the enrichment program at St. Catharines Collegiate. I shrugged and went along with it. The biggest draw was that the enrichment class would complete five days' work in four days, with an advanced critical thinking component on Friday mornings. We finished early every week—Fridays after lunch. More freedom? Count me in.

Play Hard, Dream Harder

Playing every sport I could and hanging out with friends were my primary interests in those early years. I played AAA hockey, all-star baseball, and golfed every Sunday with my family at Twenty Valley Golf and Country Club. We lived in a golden age of childhood freedom. Life was good. But adolescence brought new questions—and a deeper curiosity about who I was becoming.

High school brought its own evolution. At first, sports continued to dominate, but gradually, my energy shifted toward social life and self-discovery. Sunday nights at the Henley Hotel and Friday dances at Club 404 became formative rituals. That was also when alcohol and cannabis first entered the picture.

Many of the friendships I made back then are still with me today. There was a magic to that era: weekend house parties, semi-formals, ski trips, Club Exit in New York State, and of course, Old Port Dalhousie. The eighties were all about self-expression and exploring every imaginable freedom. It was an incredible time to be a teenager.

A Spark *in the Mind*

The turning point in school came in grade 11 with a course called Man in Society, later renamed People in Society. It wasn't just a class—it was a door. We studied philosophy, psychology, literature, and existential thought. Socrates, Descartes, Dostoyevsky, Freud, and Jung. For the first time, I experienced what it meant to be intellectually awake. Our teacher, Vaughn Osgan, wasn't just an educator—he was a guide. In many ways, this class was our *Dead Poets Society*.

That class lit a spark that turned into a slow-burning fire. It awakened something bigger than academic interest—it invited me into a deeper emotional and spiritual curiosity. Outside of school, I began reading more and exploring Eastern philosophies—Taoism, Buddhism. I started practicing transcendental meditation. I wasn't being assigned this stuff. I was drawn to it. The concepts of duality, balance, and energy flow opened my mind. I started noticing patterns everywhere—in people, in nature, in myself.

It was the first time I truly began to reflect on what it means to live well. I remember lying awake some nights, staring at the ceiling, wondering about death and time and the soul.

I felt a yearning I didn't yet have words for. A desire to live deeply and understand life fully. It wasn't religion. It wasn't dogma. It was awe.

. . .

The Summer **I Grew Old**

Reflection turned to reckoning in the summer of 1990. I had just turned 17. That was the year I lost my older brother, David, to suicide.

David had been struggling with a rare degenerative disease of the optic nerve that led to blindness. In seeking treatment, he experienced a cascade of complications causing severe hallucinations and psychosis that ultimately led to his death. His suffering was brutal. His loss was shattering.

Watching my parents grieve was something I'll never forget. My mother's hair turned white almost overnight. Our house fell silent. The world suddenly felt unstable.

David's death forever altered how I saw time, mortality, and meaning. It became a quiet compass inside me—one that would guide how I showed up for others, and eventually, how I faced my own battles. He had only been 21. I saw, in an instant, how quickly everything can vanish. How fragile the threads are. Thankfully, my girlfriend Shannon was there to help me through it. We were inseparable and her emotional support was paramount.

Mission: **Inclusion**

The hallway cliques and status games of high school started to seem ridiculous. I became more sensitive to how people treated each other. Judgment, bullying, indifference—I couldn't stand it anymore. Racism, in particular, boiled my blood. We needed more compassion. More presence. More humanity. I felt I could do something about it—and must.

That realization stirred something actionable in me. I sat down and wrote a personal mission statement. A vow to help build a more inclusive and loving community. I shared it with Betty T., our school's vice principal, and told her I wanted to run for student council president.

I also shared my vision with Jon Walsh, the smartest and kindest guy I knew. We assembled a cracker team and ran on a platform of inclusivity, positivity, and school spirit. We wanted everyone—no matter their social circle or background—to feel like they belonged.

And we delivered.

The Red Hot Chili Party — *yes, we named ourselves after the band. No, we didn't go as far as just the socks… but we definitely brought the heat.*

We organized student "buyouts" for sporting events. We filled buses and stands for intercity championship football and basketball games and won both titles that year! We hosted a Red Hot Chili eating contest, an air band competition and a battle of the bands in the school's massive auditorium. I even stepped out of my comfort zone by joining the musical production of *Pippin*. That year taught me that when people feel like they belong, they come to life—and that lesson stuck with me.

The school came alive. Something about that year taught me

that leadership isn't about authority—it's about empowerment and amplification. When people feel seen and valued, they shine.

"You see us as you want to see us… In the simplest terms, in the most convenient definitions. But what we found out is that each one of us is a brain… and an athlete… and a basket case… a princess… and a criminal."
— *The Breakfast Club*

That John Hughes classic movie lived in my bones. Everyone matters. Everyone has brilliance inside them. That was a understanding I would carry into every chapter of my life that followed —even the ones that nearly broke me.

THE BALANCING ACT

The next phase of my story begins with a new kind of responsibility—and the tight rope walking act that would shape my twenties.

When it came time to choose a university major, I gravitated toward Philosophy. But my mom, ever pragmatic, said, "Check the want ads and see how many jobs there are for philosophers." I laughed, saw her point, and pivoted to Psychology and was accepted at Brock University.

In my first-year Psych course, we started learning about synapses in the brain. Intrigued, I immediately switched my major to Neuroscience. It was a massive leap for someone with a liberal arts mind, but I loved it. Even the hard stuff. Especially the hard stuff. I was fascinated by underlying the science of how the mind works, not just experienced. This was a new world to me, and interestingly, I started to see foundational philosophical concepts like circularity, balance, and equilibrium deeply layered in chemistry, biology, and physiology. These concepts became foundational in how I perceived life and human interaction ever since.

Then life added another layer, one that would stretch every part of me. Just as I was beginning to find a rhythm between academic intensity and deeper inner exploration, Shannon became pregnant. It was a jolt into real-world adulthood—a sudden immersion into responsibility and sacrifice that I wasn't fully prepared for, but somehow welcomed. I knew everything was about to change, and I leaned in. We got married at 20, the first of our friends to start a family. Aidan was born, and I was suddenly balancing university, part-time jobs, diapers, and the weight of figuring out who I was.

We later welcomed Niall and Lauren into our family in our little home on Russell Ave. I was learning how to be a husband, a father, a provider, and a student—all at once—while still making time for fun, friends, and sports.

When the Brain Says No

In my final year at Brock, I completed a research thesis on neurotransmitter interactions resulting in epileptic seizure responses in rats. The science fascinated me, and it was for a great cause. But performing surgery on living animals, inducing seizures, observing and recording them, then dissecting their brains—that part crushed me. I finished the study and published the data, but I knew, deep in my gut, that I couldn't spend my life doing work that came at that kind of ethical cost.

Instead, I found other ways to contribute. I taught classes for Epilepsy Niagara, helping families understand the condition and showing them how meditation could reduce stress and improve quality of life. I would later go on to develop a US patent for an early detection epileptic warning device in the form factor of a hearing aid in my mid-30s. I never did much with my Neuroscience degree professionally, but it wasn't all for nothing.

Finishing university didn't bring clarity. I had three kids to support and no roadmap. I tried selling life insurance. It was a disaster. I lasted a year and ended up $6,000 in debt.

My mom, then working at Niagara College, brought home a course guide. One of the programs—Electronic Engineering Technology—jumped out at me. It promised employable skills. I applied and got in. Between the ages of 16–26, I had jumped from liberal arts to human sciences, all the way to physical sciences—all while raising a young family, working part time in the service industry, and still having altogether too much fun with my friends and social life. It was a lot to manage.

Sleep was optional. Stress was constant. It was a crucible—and eventually, it cracked my marriage.

At 29, Shannon asked for a divorce.

The Fall and the First Rebuild

That moment hit like a freight train. I had been trying to keep the wheels on, to stay strong for the kids, to build some kind of future—but the truth was, I was barely holding it together. My self-confidence collapsed. I felt unworthy, ashamed, uncertain of everything. It was soul-crushing.

The next three years were the darkest of my life. I spiralled. I drank too much. Smoked too much weed. Stayed up too late. I tried endless dating, but nothing stuck. I felt lost in a world that seemed to be moving on without me.

This was also the period when we lost my mother's lifelong best friend—my Godmother, Lana Thompson—after a ten-year battle with cancer. Lana was a legend in our family and our community, with more positive energy than most people will ever know. No matter how hard things got, she radiated love and carried a lively, uplifting spirit.

Her battle with cancer—while also going through a divorce at the same time I was—became a powerful source of inspiration. Watching her navigate both with grace, humour, and an unwavering will to live reminded me of what true resilience looked like. She would often crack jokes during chemo, make time to call and check on others, and keep showing up with love no matter how exhausted she felt. That kind of strength was contagious. In my lowest moments, I'd remember her laugh, her courage, her ability to hold light in the darkest rooms—and it helped me start searching for my own courage and strength for myself. It was the first time cancer had touched my life, and I saw firsthand the gruelling toll that chemotherapy can take on a person.

Her passing in 2004 marked a turning point. In the wake of her death, I made a quiet but firm commitment to pull myself out of the depression I had been drowning in and find healthier ways to cope. I turned to hiking, mountain biking, meditation—anything that helped reconnect me with life and a sense of peace.

THE SACRED WEEKENDS

Little by little, I began to rebuild—not just as a young professional, but as a single father in his mid-thirties, determined to find meaning and momentum again. I focused on my kids. Every weekend with them became sacred. We went on adventures, built forts, and had movie marathons. I did my best to make our time magical.

Professionally, I landed at Gennum Corporation—first in manufacturing, then in engineering, and finally settling in sales. I traveled, hustled, and grew into my role. That's when I got the chance to help launch the first noise-cancelling Bluetooth headset in Canada. I found myself flying coast to coast, closing deals, reigniting old friendships, and falling in love with British Columbia. The pace was thrilling, but it wasn't just about the external wins—it was helping rebuild my inner sense of worth. Every new relationship, every closed deal, every new city reminded me that I could still create, still contribute, still grow. I began to feel momentum again—not just in my career, but in my sense of purpose.

Gennum sent me to work in New York City in the summer of 2007. I reconnected with Randy Robles, a childhood friend. We talked music, life, dreams. We golfed, we played poker and went out 4-5 nights a week. I even wrote a song: "Breakfast in Hoboken." The momentum was real. This is one of the most memorable and funnest summers of my life.

"Life moves pretty fast. If you don't stop and look around once in a while, you could miss it."
— *Ferris Bueller, Ferris Bueller's Day Off*

People Over Profit

Then came BlueAnt, an upstart Australian tech company. I helped grow them into Canada's top Bluetooth brand. But when promised compensation never came, I walked away. I had tasted success, but I needed purpose. More importantly, I committed myself to working for companies that valued ethics and people over profit.

That's when Hitfar entered the picture. I joined Troy Fargey's team and found a kindred spirit. Someone who cared about doing things right. We built something meaningful together.

The Leap at 41

In 2014, at 41, I made a bold decision: I sold my house, packed up, and moved to Vancouver. My kids supported it. They knew I needed this. Most of my friends had young families, and my kids were now young adults. I had exhausted every avenue of self-expression and learning. But more than that, I was hungry for reinvention. I needed to immerse myself in something new—new geography, new energy, new possibilities. A deeper part of me knew that staying would mean slowly fading. Moving was not just a change of scenery; it was a lifeline. It was time for a fresh start.

I loved living in B.C. I hiked and mountain biked the coastal mountain trails. I summited many mountaintops with my dog, Shadow. I was writing new original music again. I swam in the ocean. I joined a beach volleyball league. I made great new friends. I explored every major stretch of highway B.C. has to offer, multiple times. I was feeling more alive, happy, and content than any other period of my life.

Slash and the Sacred Bond

Then came D'Arcy. My soulmate.

We met through mutual friend, Kelsey Powers on Halloween

2016. D'Arcy was dressed as Slash. I was smitten. We started dating six months later and moved in after just one month. When you know, you know.

She brought light, laughter, and grounding into my life. She challenged me to grow and loved me as I was. Her loyalty has never wavered and to this day she is my greatest source of strength, confidence, compassion and resilience.

The Circular Setting Sun

On June 21, 2019, I found myself working in Whitehorse, Yukon. I hadn't planned to be there on the summer solstice—it just worked out that way, almost like the universe had an appointment with me. I drove north along the Klondike Highway, chasing the midnight sun, surrounded by a vast, untouched wilderness that felt ancient and sacred.

On the longest day of the year, I pulled over, stood by the side of the road, and watched the sun set and rise in the same breath. The sky glowed with a surreal golden hue that seemed to hold a message.

I cried. Something clicked. In that suspended moment between day and night, light and shadow, I saw my life stretched out behind me—and a future that needed redirection. My life needed to change.

This was the moment I knew I needed to do something more than chase experiences of the natural world. I needed to transition my focus to something more altruistic, good for humanity.

Enter: Eco-Train

About a month later, while hiking through Belcarra Park in

Port Moody, B.C., the idea for Eco-Train arrived like a whisper from the forest. It wasn't just a business idea—it was a mission: help heal the planet through circular economy and environmental awareness.

I built a concept for a material recovery program for the wireless industry in Canada and pitched it to Hitfar and their customer base. It took seven months of intense work on top of my regular day job, but on March 17, 2020—Global Recycling Day—Eco-Train was ready for national launch.

The industry was excited. I was pumped.

Momentum Meets Pandemic

Two weeks later—COVID hit.

The retail sector basically shut down for two years. No one had time for sustainability. I tried to keep it going out of pocket. TELUS, Bell, and Loblaws expressed interest, but the momentum fizzled. After three years, there were a few hundred participating retailers, but I had to admit: the program had plateaued. I was depleted.

Frontotemporal Dementia and the Long Goodbye

At the same time, my father's FTD took hold. It is a cruel disease. It stole his empathy, his humour, his very essence. I flew back and forth to Ontario constantly to support my mom and help navigate long-term care.

It was devastating. We lost him piece by piece. The whole thing was frustrating, sad, and extremely challenging to say the least.

. . .

SUPDOCK: The Lightness Between Storms

SUPDOCK Prototype

In 2023, a lighter idea bubbled up: SUPDOCK. A playful, electric motorized, floating hangout for paddle boarders and dreamers. I needed that spark of creativity and a new business idea. It gave me joy.

But even as I worked on it, something deeper was shifting in my body. Something was growing.

WHAT CAME NEXT WOULD CHANGE everything.

CHAPTER 2

SOMETHING'S NOT RIGHT

"Don't panic, but the world's about to end…"
— Radiohead, *"Planet Telex"*

In the summer of 2022, I began experiencing something strange: periodic nausea and dry heaving after smoking cannabis or drinking coffee—symptoms I had never encountered before, despite a long and familiar relationship with both. Around the same time, I started noticing occasional spots of blood on the toilet paper after bowel movements. It wasn't frequent—maybe every couple of months—but it was enough to make me pause.

By April 2023, I decided it was time to seek medical advice. I didn't have a family doctor, so I visited a local walk-in clinic. The physician ordered blood work and a stool sample to check for cancer markers and other health indicators typical for a man in his early 50s.

A few weeks later, I received a call: everything looked great. I was in excellent health for my age. I exhaled. *Relief.*

Fast forward six months. It's a weekend getaway in Sooke, B.C.—me, D'Arcy, Sean, Andrea, Alex, Raji, Lindsay and Heather—our lifelong friend gang from St. Catharines. Three days of fun, drinks, and celebration. But on the final morning, I woke up feeling brutal. A severe hangover, coupled with a sharp, uncomfortable pain in my abdomen. Hoping to shake it off, I made my way to the bathroom. That's when everything changed. The toilet filled with blood. Not a trace. Not a streak. It was *full*.

I froze, staring in disbelief. My body went cold.

I called out to D'Arcy and told her what had happened. She didn't hesitate—*we're going to the hospital.* We quickly packed our bags, said a brief goodbye to our friends, and headed straight to Victoria General, the nearest hospital, 45 minutes up the road.

We arrived at the Emergency around 11 a.m. I checked in and explained everything to the triage nurse. Then began the wait. Five hours passed in the waiting area. Blood was drawn at some point, but otherwise, it was just me, the discomfort, and the growing sense that something was wrong.

When I finally saw the doctor, he told me the bloodwork looked great—which brought a flicker of relief. Still, he recommended a CT scan to rule out anything serious.

Another three hours passed before I was called in for the scan.

A Shadow in the Scan

Eventually, the doctor returned with the results. He said everything looked normal *except* for one thing: a small shadow—just a faint one—near the junction where the small intestine meets the large intestine.

He suspected it could be diverticulitis. The bleeding? Possibly an internal hemorrhoid. He told me it likely wasn't anything serious. Nothing urgent.

Just to be safe, he suggested I follow up with a gastroenterologist for a colonoscopy when I got back to Vancouver.

After the long day at Victoria General Hospital, we left feeling encouraged by the initial results. Although we spent 12 hours in the emergency room, the blood work and CT scan indicated no immediate concerns. This experience, however, set off a chain of events that would ultimately change my life forever going forward.

When I returned from Vancouver Island, I went to the local walk-in clinic to follow up on the doctor's recommendation for a colonoscopy. The doctor there arranged the appointment but mentioned that the wait time would be 2-3 months.

A WINDOW of Normalcy

In the two months that followed, I was relatively stress-free. I carried on with my daily life, reassured by the negative results from the blood work and CT scan. I viewed the upcoming colonoscopy as merely a precaution and redirected my focus toward developing SUPDOCK.

SUPDOCK: A Spark of Joy

I developed the prototype for for use with paddles and small electric motors. The prototype measured 4X2 metres. It could hold up to eight people, comfortably accommodating four people in lawn chairs. The dock featured a 4-speed motor, controlled with a Bluetooth remote, capable of reaching speeds of up to 9 km/h.

The compact design allowed it to be stored easily in a standard closet at home.

I ordered a variety of docks, motors, and accessories to test different prototypes. I tested them on the water—even braving the winter cold in a wetsuit. I developed a business case to assess the viability and began working with my daughter Lauren, a graphic designer, to build the website: **supdock.ca**.

To celebrate D'Arcy's birthday, we planned 10-day vacation to Sayulita, Mexico, February 4-15, 2024. We were excited! Life was on an upward trajectory again. Before the vacation, we spent Christmas in Revelstoke, B.C. with Aidan, his wife Linda, and my two grandsons, Oliver and Noah. The week was amazing. We had a great time.

THE PRECAUTION BECOMES *Real*

A few weeks after Christmas, I received a phone call about the colonoscopy appointment. It was scheduled for January 20, 2024, with Dr. Henry Cassman. While I had initially viewed the procedure as a precaution, the reality of the appointment began to settle in. I started to feel a little bit anxious about possible negative outcomes.

THE COLONOSCOPY

The procedure happened January 24, 2024. I entered the specialized "Colonoscopy" room, where I was greeted by a nurse and Dr. Cassman. After receiving a light sedation through an IV, they prepared me for the procedure. The doctor inserted a flexible colonoscope, approximately four feet long and half an inch in diameter, into my rectum. At the end of the tube was a high-resolution digital camera along with a thin wire snare designed for snipping off any polyps discovered during the examination. The entire process was displayed on a monitor beside the bed. I watched the the whole procedure as it unfolded.

As the doctor navigated the colonoscope, the first thing encountered was a hemorrhoid, which he figured was the most likely cause of the blood I experienced. This was somewhat reassuring to me. However, as the examination continued deeper into the colon, the doctor discovered a small polyp. I was intrigued by how smoothly the doctor maneuvered the snare to capture the polyp. The quick action of severing it from the colon wall and sucking it up the vacuum tube was a fascinating sight. I was impressed by the medical technology and the skill involved in the procedure.

After removing the initial polyp, Dr. Cassman continued the colonoscopy, advancing the colonoscope deeper into my colon. About two feet in from the anus, we encountered what appeared to be a larger polyp. The doctor attempted to snare and remove it, explaining, "This doesn't look cancerous, but let's get a biopsy just to be safe."

Dr. Cassman ordered another blood screening test to check for cancer markers, reassuring me as I got dressed that I could expect the results in 7-10 days. Feeling somewhat assured that the bleeding was likely due to an internal hemorrhoid and that the polyps were not a major concern, I left the hospital with a sense of relief.

During the week following the colonoscopy, D'Arcy and I focused on the upcoming vacation in Sayulita. Life felt good, filled with excitement and anticipation for the upcoming trip. We were both optimistic, believing that I had nothing to worry about.

A week later, Dr. Cassman called with the results of the blood work. He said, "Bloodwork looks good. There's no sign of cancer. I'm still waiting for the results of the biopsy, but I'm 99% sure it's not cancerous. Don't worry about anything. Don't lose any sleep. I'll call you with the results as soon as I have them." I felt a wave of relief, reinforcing my belief that the situation was under control.

The Diagnosis

Three days later everything changed. Dr. Cassman called again, and this time his tone was serious. "Mr. Cain, I'm sorry to inform you, you have colon cancer." My heart sank. The words echoed in my mind, and I glanced at D'Arcy, who was equally taken aback. The biopsy had revealed cancer cells, and what they had assumed was just a polyp was actually a 4 cm cancerous tumour.

Dr. Cassman explained the urgency of the situation: the tumour needed to be removed as soon as possible. He indicated that I could expect a call from a surgeon within a week or two. After the call ended, I found myself in a state of shock. The next ten minutes after receiving the diagnosis were a whirlwind of confusion and emotion. The weight of the news hit me hard; the word "cancer" echoed in my mind and D'Arcy and I looked at each other in disbelief. We embraced tightly, allowing ourselves a moment to cry and absorb the gravity of the situation. I held onto a glimmer of hope that the tumour would be benign and that routine surgery could resolve the issue. Reflecting on the circumstances, I felt grateful that the bleeding from the hemorrhoid had prompted me to seek medical attention, ultimately leading to the detection of the cancer.

. . .

The Familiar Face

My case was referred to Dr. Sue Sanderson, a general surgeon based in New Westminster, B.C.. This felt like a serendipitous turn of events, as I had a history with Dr. Sanderson. Three years prior, she performed an emergency appendectomy on me after my appendix burst in the waiting area of Eagle Ridge Hospital in Coquitlam, B.C. I remembered her fondly and felt relieved and grateful for her skilled hands that night, believing she had already saved my life once. I felt a sense of comfort knowing that Dr. Sanderson would be overseeing my care.

Three days later, we met with Dr. Sanderson in her office. She recognized me immediately. I expressed my gratitude once more for her previous care during the appendectomy. The conversation took a more serious turn aconfirmed the presence of the 4 cm cancerous tumour on my ascending colon. She went on to explain that after reviewing my previous CT scans, she noticed some shading or small spots around the omentum—a thin, fatty layer covering the abdominal organs. To better assess the situation, she ordered another CT scan.

We were leaving for Sayulita in 4 days. The CT scan happened three days later. Things were moving quickly. Dr. Sanderson said she'd call me four days later with the results. OK, we thought, we'll deal with the news once we get the results. At the time, we decided to enjoy the vacation.

Sayulita

The timing of the trip to Sayulita was a welcome distraction from the stress of the impending medical news. We arrived in Sayulita Feb 7, 2024. It was beautiful warm and sunny day. We got ourselves settled into a small suite just a ten-minute walk from the main square and took full advantage of our time there. Over the next three days, we immersed ourselves in the vibrant culture, strolling through the cobblestone streets, relaxing on the beaches, and enjoying the outdoor patios.

Sayulita - Day 2

On the 4th day we rented a golf cart for 24 hours, allowing us to explore all the local beaches, visit the nearby cemetery, and cruise all over town. We swam, played in the waves, soaked up the sun, all while trying to keep our minds off the uncertainty of the cancer diagnosis.

The Fateful Call

Later that day, everything changed. While sitting poolside on the patio at our Air BnB, I received the call I had been dreading. Nervously, I answered the phone, and Dr. Sanderson's somber voice filled the line. She delivered the devastating news that the cancer had spread to my omentum and potentially other areas around my abdomen.

Dr. Sanderson informed me that my condition was at least stage 3, which meant that the procedure to remove the tumour was beyond her practice. She needed to consult with cecal cancer specialists. My heart sank as she explained that I should expect a combination of chemotherapy and complex abdominal surgery over the next several months. We agreed to meet with her when we got home from Mexico to discuss the next steps and the treatment plan.

CONFRONTING *the Reality of Cancer*

After hanging up, I looked at D'Arcy, and tears welled up in my eyes. I could see the sadness mirrored in her expression. We embraced tightly, allowing our emotions to take hold. The gravity of the situation sank in deeper. I thought about my parents, who had already lost my older brother David; The thought of them losing both of us was unbearable.

I thought of my children Aidan, Niall and Lauren. How do I tell them? The tears came a little harder. They are adults now, 31, 29 and 25 at the time, but still. This news was going to worry my family immensely. I thought of my friends, all the people in my life, my dreams and aspirations, my time here in this earthly existence. The prospect of dying from cancer weighed heavy on me. That can't happen, I thought. So, it's not happening.

I took a few moments to pull myself together. I had to share the news with my mom first, knowing she had been anxiously awaiting the update. She listened intently as I explained the diagnosis. To my relief, she handled the news with remarkable strength and wisdom.

"Sounds like the prognosis is treatable," she reassured me. "Stage 3 is not stage 4 or terminal cancer. This will be a challenging year, but you can do it." Her words offered me a glimmer of hope amid the turmoil. I asked her to inform my children about the diagnosis, knowing I would struggle to do it without breaking down. She agreed to call each of them to explain the situation in a way that would minimize their worries.

FINDING SOLACE **at the Beach**

With the golf cart rented until 8 AM the next day, we decided to make the most of our time in Sayulita. We drove to Carricitos Beach and found a quiet, private spot to relax. Tucked away from the wind beside some large, jagged rock formations, we settled onto our towels and opened a cocktail.

Sitting in this serene environment, I drew some deep breaths, allowing the beauty and the sounds of the beach to wash over me. I listened to the waves and reflected on the reality of the situation. "This is going to be the hardest year of my life," I thought, I reassured myself, "I got this, I can do it and I must do it"

I strolled up and down the beach, contemplating my life and the challenges ahead. Despite the weight of the diagnosis, I was struck by the beauty of my surroundings. I reminded myself of the importance of gratitude, recognizing that I was in a stunning place with hours of sunlight left to enjoy. The song Breakdown popped into my head.

---

*"But you can't stop nothing
If you got no control
Of the thoughts in your mind
That you kept in, you know."*
— Jack Johnson, "Breakdown"

Feeling hungry, I returned to where D'Arcy was sitting. We packed up our things, hopped back in the golf cart, and headed into town for tacos and margaritas. We tried to make the most of the remainder of our day, while dealing with the shock of the diagnosis.

A Long Sleepless Night

That first night was one of deep turmoil for me. I tossed and turned, unable to sleep as my mind spiralled into a vortex of fear and anxiety. Questions flooded my thoughts: What if my life is cut short? Up until now, what have I accomplished? I felt sad and disappointed with a deep sense of urgency, realizing I hadn't yet reached my personal or professional potential. The weight of my ambitions not yet realized pressed heavily on me. There's so much more I need to do. I need to be there for D'Arcy, my parents, children, grandchildren and friends. The thought of dying and leaving everyone behind was unbearable. My mind became a tangled mess of worry, concern and fear. I didn't sleep a wink that night.

The next morning, I shared my emotional distress with D'Arcy. She listened attentively, her confidence and unwavering support shining through, as she always does. She reassured me, saying, "If anyone can beat cancer, it's you." She reminded me of my strength and resilience. "Have you met Bob Cain?" she asked playfully. "Piece of cake. You will crush this. I guarantee it." Her encouragement helped to lift some of the weight off my shoulders. I'm so grateful for her presence in my life, knowing that I have a partner who believes in me and loves me wholeheartedly.

Feeling a little better, it was time to call each of my children to discuss the news. They were all loving and supportive. I emphasized the cancer was treatable and that I would beat it. Their responses were reassuring; they expressed unwavering belief in me and encouraged me not to worry. Each conversation provided a sense of relief. I started to feel a sense of hope amid the chaos from the previous night.

INFORMING *Friends - Building a Support Network*

Next, I started informing my closest friends about my diagnosis. I wanted to keep the news within a small circle for the time being, opting to share it with my family and closest friends before going public. I created five group text chats—one for family and four others for unique interconnected groups of friends.

As I sent out the messages about my diagnosis, I felt a surprising sense of empowerment. Sharing the news was the first step in building my support tribe—the people who would stand by me in the battle ahead. It was a pivotal moment, both mentally and socially. I was grateful I opened up, because knowing the people closest to me were willing to carry some of the emotional weight made the burden feel lighter.

. . .

A Transformative Conversation

The day after sharing my diagnosis with my closest friends, I received a phone call from Randy in New York. I felt a surge of happiness upon hearing from him as I knew he would lighten the mood.

The conversation began somberly, touching on the gravity of my situation. However, he soon shifted the tone, delivering words that would significantly alter my perspective on my cancer journey. "You know what, Bobnocerous? This is an incredible opportunity for you," He emphasized that while I had faced difficult challenges before, nothing compared to the monumental task of beating cancer.

Randy's words resonated deeply. "You have an opportunity to kick cancer's ass and show the world how it's done," he continued, instilling a sense of empowerment and hope. He encouraged me to embrace the moment as a opportunity for growth and inspiration. "You're going to inspire your family, friends, and a lot of people with your story," he added.

I realized that Randy was presenting me with a new way to think about the cancer diagnosis. Instead of viewing it as a daunting, frightening prognosis, I could choose to see it as a pivotal moment for personal transformation. Randy urged me to become singularly focused beating cancer and to forget everything else. "You don't have to worry about any of the other daily stresses and worries that weigh most people down. All you must do is focus on beating cancer. That's all, that's it. And, you'll gain great strength and wisdom in doing so," he concluded. Lastly, he said "Bob 1.0 is awesome, but I can't wait to see Bob 2.0."

Over the course of that ten-minute phone call, I felt the heavy fog of worry, fear, and concern dissipate. My path forward became crystal clear. Inspired by Randy's perspective, I resolved to kick cancer's ass and show the world how it could be done. From that moment on, I felt 100% confident I would win my battle with cancer. The anxiety that plagued me during the first night was replaced by a positive mental attitude singularly focused on beating and becoming a better, stronger and wiser version of myself. My circumstance had transformed from a dark and scary challenge into the opportunity of a lifetime.

After we hung up the phone, D'Arcy hugged me tightly, sensing the shift in mindset. We smiled and laughed together, feeling a renewed sense of hope and determination. With our heads a little lighter, we packed some supplies and set out to make the most of our time in Sayulita.

A New Resolve

Later that day when we stopped for margaritas, I decided to give myself the best fighting chance against cancer, I needed to approach the battle sober. I resolved to abstain from alcohol and cannabis until I had clearly beaten cancer. This marked the beginning of a year of sobriety for me, a commitment I hadn't made since my teenage years of partying.

With this new mindset, we embraced our vacation. We were determined to enjoy each moment, knowing that uncertainty lay ahead. I felt fortunate that I had no noticeable cancer symptoms; I wasn't in pain, and I had plenty of energy.

24HrDay is Born

We chose to focus on the present rather than worrying about potential challenges down the road. This "one step at a time-one day at a time" perspective became the foundation for this book.

24HrDay became my mantra, constantly reminding myself to control the things I could control and not to get lost in worry or fear about the future or really anything outside my control.

As the trip ended, I felt grateful for D'Arcy's unwavering support. She would accompany me to every single appointment throughout the year—a total of 86 appointments including consultations with various doctors, nurses, dieticians, social workers, blood work sessions, imaging procedures, multiple surgeries, and numerous wound care sessions. The journey ahead was going to be intense and challenging, but I knew I wouldn't face it alone. With this understanding, we returned home from Sayulita, ready to tackle whatever came next, knowing we had each other and a solid plan to approach the year ahead with positivity and strength.

CHAPTER 3

TREATMENT STRATEGY AND FAMILY TIME

"Home is when I'm with You."
— Edward Sharpe & The Magnetic Zeros

BEACHSIDE RESOLVE IN SAYULITA

The last few days in Sayulita were great. We explored the town and relaxed at the beaches. We spent quality time together, allowing ourselves to genuinely enjoy the trip despite the gravity of the cancer diagnosis. Days spent lounging quietly on the beach, soaking in the sun, and listening to the soothing sound of waves crashing against the shore felt like a massage for my soul. It was awesome.

As I continued to reflect on my situation, I felt an overwhelming desire to live. "Dying is not an option," I resolved. I have faith in the Canadian healthcare system and the advancements in modern Western medicine available for cancer treatment. This conviction fuelled my determination to face the challenges ahead, overcome cancer, and emerge with a renewed sense of purpose.

I envisioned myself living to the age of 100, feeling confident that I still had another 50 years ahead of me. This optimistic outlook became the driving force behind my motivation to act. I was committed to doing everything in my power to fight this disease and embrace life fully.

Taking Control: My Personal Health Strategy

I began considering ways I could personally contribute to my fight against cancer. I identified several key areas I could make a positive impact on my health:

Physical Fitness and Mental Health: Recognizing the importance of my physical and mental well-being, I would exercise daily. I figured that extensive chemotherapy would eventually make exercise impossible, so I aimed to take advantage of my ability at that moment and to stay active for as long as I was able to.

Dietary Improvements: I committed to enhancing my diet by ensuring I consumed at least 60 grams of protein, two servings of vegetables, and one serving of fruit every day. The decision to eliminate alcohol and cannabis was also a significant step in prioritizing my health.

Yoga and Mindfulness: To improve my mobility and flexibility, I vowed myself to practice yoga more frequently. I also made a commitment to meditate regularly and to intentionally foster a daily positive mental attitude throughout my journey.

Mental Resilience: I devoted myself to eliminate negative thought patterns that fostered fear, worry, and concern. I recognized that these emotional states could lead to increased stress, anxiety, and depression, all of which would hinder me in my battle against cancer.

With these actionable steps in place, I felt empowered. I had a strategy. Upon returning home from Sayulita, I felt relaxed and ready to face the next steps in my cancer journey.

Aidan's Visit **and the SUPDOCK Adventure**

My oldest son Aidan lives in Revelstoke, B.C. with his wife Linda and sons, Oliver and Noah. It's a six-hour drive to Vancouver but he immediately came to see me after we got home. I was very touched he dropped everything to come see me right away when he learned the news of my diagnosis. To make the most of our time together, we decided to test one of the SUPDOCK's by taking a cruise around Indian Arm. Although the weather was still quite cool, it was a beautiful, sunny day, perfect for an adventure on the water.

We launched from Bedwell Bay and paddled a round trip to Twin Islands, covering about 12 kilometres. Along the way, we dropped a crab trap, baited with four raw chicken thighs—turns out, crabs love chicken. By the time we pulled it up, the bait was gone, and we had a decent haul. We kept three that were large enough and let the rest go, watching them drop back into the deep.

Bob and Aidan on the SUPDOCK *Test #2 was a success—solid, stable, and smiles all around.*

Aidan is a Red Seal chef with a catering business. His culinary skills transformed our catch into a delicious dinner. The meal was not only a testament to our successful crabbing adventure but also a heartwarming reminder of the bond we share as father and son. I savoured the deliciousness of the meal, feeling grateful for the time spent with Aidan.

During Aidan's visit, we took the opportunity to talk openly about the cancer diagnosis. We shared our thoughts and feelings, and I greatly appreciated Aidan's unwavering confidence in my ability to beat the disease.

Aidan, with his calm demeanour, conveyed a sense of certainty that reassured me and helped alleviate some of the weight I felt from the diagnosis.

I'm incredibly proud of Aidan and the man he's become. He's an excellent husband, father, brother, friend, and son. There's a calmness and quiet cool about him that draws people in—and he'll bend over backwards for the ones he loves. He puts all he has into everything he does. Over the years, we've developed a close and meaningful friendship. And you know, I realize now that the day Shannon and I learned we were expecting at 19 was perhaps the single most pivotal moment of my life.

Consultation #2 with Dr. Sanderson

A few days after Aidan's visit, D'Arcy and I met with Dr. Sanderson for a follow-up consultation. She reviewed everything we had discussed during the previous phone call, emphasizing the importance of understanding the treatment plan. Dr. Sanderson presented the images from the latest CT scan, showing us, the small spots scattered around my omentum along with two swollen lymph nodes that would need to be removed with their connected arteries.

Dr. Sanderson outlined the initial treatment plan, consisting of 24 weeks (12 cycles) of chemotherapy. The primary goal of this regimen was to slow down and hopefully stop the cancer from spreading further. We listened intently as she explained the intricacies of the plan, feeling a mix of anxiety and determination. Provided the chemotherapy was effective and the cancer did not spread, I would then undergo Cytoreductive/HIPEC surgery to remove any remaining cancer from my abdomen.

This was the first time I had heard of HIPEC surgery, so Dr. Sanderson took the time to explain the procedure in detail. The procedure would involve a specialized surgeon opening my abdomen to carefully examine and remove any visible cancer. After this meticulous surgical procedure, my entire abdominal cavity would be saturated with a heated chemotherapy bath for 60-90 minutes.

There are only three surgeons in British Columbia qualified to perform HIPEC surgery. I didn't know it at the time, but I would be treated by all three of them over the next six months. Dr. Sanderson advised me that Dr. Andrea MacNeill at Vancouver General Hospital (VGH) would be overseeing my case going forward and that she would conduct the surgery. This provided me with a sense of reassurance knowing I would be in capable hands.

Additionally, Dr. Sanderson mentioned Dr. Lina Lua, a medical oncologist with BC Cancer, would coordinate the chemotherapy treatment plan. This helped to alleviate some of my anxiety, and I appreciated Dr. Sanderson's assurance that I would receive the best possible care.

After the consultation, we had a clearer understanding of what lay ahead. We recognized that the year would be very long and challenging. The plan was now in place, we just had to tackle it, one step at a time. One day at a time.

I continued to provide regular updates to my family and friends after each consultation. The emotional support I received from them was huge for me. I felt very fortunate to have a strong support network. The laughter and light-hearted conversations were very therapeutic, helping me to maintain a positive outlook. My friends often reassured me, saying, "If anyone can do it, you can," which helped bolster my confidence to win the battle.

While I had been updating my inner circle, I hadn't made the news of my cancer diagnosis public. I needed more time to process the situation before sharing it with a wider audience, including other friends, business associates, and acquaintances. I was aware that the news would eventually spread, and I wanted to control the narrative rather than let it be distorted through the rumour mill. I decided I would make a public statement on social media when the time was right, but not quite yet.

. . .

More Visits from Family and Friends

My son Niall, along with two of my best friends, Mark and Sean, came to visit me next. It had been a few weeks since I had seen Aidan, so I was thrilled to spend time with them. The day after their scheduled departure, my mother arranged to spend two weeks with me. Additionally, my daughter Lauren agreed to join us for the last five days of my mom's visit. They all flew in from Ontario.

I was looking forward to three exciting weeks filled with good company and fun times before my chemotherapy treatments began. Precious time with family and friends ensured my spirits were lifted, giving me greater strength for the battle that lay ahead. The laughter, shared stories, and cherished moments helped reinforce my resolve to fight this battle with positivity and strength.

Niall, Bob, Sean, and Mark *A week together with these guys and an overnighter at Golden Ears with these guys was unforgettable— a cold night at -1 °C, but nothing could freeze the fun.*

Building a Care Team

On March 6, 2024, my mom arrived for a two-week visit. The next day D'Arcy, my mom and I met with Dr. Lina Lua to discuss my chemotherapy plan. Dr. Lua outlined that I would undergo a total of 12 treatment cycles over a 24-week period, with treatments scheduled every two weeks at Surrey Memorial Hospital, specifically within the BC Cancer Center.

During our meeting, I learned that I would need to have a PORT-A-CATH device surgically implanted into my chest. This device, about the size of a chocolate ROLO, contains a pump that administers chemotherapy drugs into a vein in my neck. This allows the medication to flow directly to my heart and be distributed throughout my body.

THE CHEMOTHERAPY COCKTAIL

Next, Dr. Lua detailed the specific drug combination that would make up my chemotherapy regimen, referred to as **GIFFOXB**:

GI: Gastrointestinal

FFOXB: Fluorouracil, Folinic Acid, Oxaliplatin, Bevacizumab

Dr. Lua explained how the individual components of this "chemo cocktail" worked together to combat cancer:

Fluorouracil (5-FU): This drug is a chemotherapy agent that inhibits cancer cell growth by interfering with their ability to replicate DNA. It specifically targets rapidly dividing cells, which is characteristic of cancer cells.

Folinic Acid: Often used in conjunction with Fluorouracil, Folinic Acid enhances the effectiveness of the chemotherapy by stabilizing the drug's binding to its target. This helps to maximize the impact on cancer cells while reducing side effects.

Oxaliplatin: This platinum-based drug works by introducing DNA cross-links, which prevent cancer cells from dividing properly. By damaging the DNA of cancer cells, Oxaliplatin helps to slow down or stop tumor growth.

Bevacizumab: This medication is a monoclonal antibody that inhibits the growth of blood vessels that supply tumours (a process known as angiogenesis). By cutting off the tumour's blood supply, Bevacizumab can help starve the cancer and inhibit its growth.

Dr. Lua's thorough explanation of how these drugs work individually and together helped me understand the rationale behind my treatment plan. She emphasized that this combination therapy was designed to destroy or limit the growth of cancer cells in my body.

The drugs would be administered directly into the PORT-A-CATH bi-weekly over the course of 24 weeks at the BC Cancer

Clinic. I should expect to spend approximately 4.5 hours in the clinic for each treatment session. Additionally, after each chemotherapy treatment in the hospital, I would receive an extra dose of fluorouracil that would be delivered over the following 46 hours using a disposable infusion device known as an INFUSOR or "baby bottle" worn on my hip.

Chemo Routine, Potential Side Effects and Recovery

Before each treatment cycle, a blood test would be necessary 1-2 days in advance to monitor my health. Additionally, a nurse would check my blood pressure before each treatment session, and a urine test would be conducted before every second treatment on even-numbered cycles. Dr. Lua explained that the dosage and timing of the chemotherapy could be adjusted based on my blood counts and any side effects I might experience.

For the first two sessions, I'd return to the hospital to have the infusion bottle removed from my PORT-A-CATH. After that, I'd be trained to remove it myself at home. Each round would be followed by a 12-day recovery period. As long as the treatment helped and side effects stayed manageable, we'd keep going.

Understanding the potential effects was critical, as it helped me prepare for what to expect during my treatment. Here are some of the side effects I might encounter:

- **Respiratory Issues:** Difficulty breathing or swallowing.
- **Allergic Reactions:** Potential allergic responses to the medication.
- **Gastrointestinal Symptoms:** Nausea, vomiting, diarrhea, and constipation.

- **_Neurological Symptoms:_** Tingling or loss of feeling in the hands, feet, nose, and throat; sensitivity to cold.
- **_Oral Health Issues_:** Sore mouth, mouth sores (canker sores), or bleeding gums.
- **_Blood Health:_** Decreased white blood cells, increased risk of infection, and blood clots.
- **_Cardiovascular Concerns_:** Increased blood pressure during treatment, abnormal heart rhythm, and heart problems.
- **_Fatigue:_** Tiredness and lack of energy.
- **_Hair Loss_:** While uncommon with fluorouracil, it could still occur.
- **_Skin Reactions_:** Skin rashes and increased sensitivity to sunburn.
- **_Appetite Changes_:** Loss of appetite.

As Dr. Lua detailed the potential side effects of the chemotherapy, I found myself feeling overwhelmed. The extensive list of frightening possibilities was daunting, and I could feel myself beginning to zone out as the information washed over me. Thankfully, D'Arcy was there to support me. She took diligent notes and asked most of the questions, ensuring we both understood the treatment process. I was still grappling with the shock of diagnosis, and in retrospect, much of the conversation is a blur.

Next Steps: *PET Scan and Chemotherapy Information Session*

Dr. Lua ordered a PET scan to get more detailed imaging of

my abdomen before chemotherapy began. This scan would help provide a clearer picture of the cancer's extent. The scan would take place within the next week or two.

Additionally, a chemotherapy information session was scheduled on Zoom the following week. During this session, the nurse from BC Cancer explained in greater detail what I could expect before, during, and after each chemotherapy session. This was reassuring, as it gave me an opportunity to gather more information and clarify any lingering questions.

The PORT-A CATH insertion surgery would happen in the next few days, and the chemotherapy sessions would commence about a week after that. While the amount of information was substantial, the clarity provided by Dr. Lua about the treatment plan was helpful. I recognized once again that I simply needed to take things step by step, one day at a time starting with the upcoming port surgery.

As we left the appointment, we all felt a mix of emotions. There was shock, relief, and a sense of awe regarding everything that was about to transpire over the next several months. I was happy to have D'Arcy and my Mom there to support me. We all understood more clearly that the journey ahead would be challenging, but at least the treatment plan was now in place.

Time with Loved Ones Before the Storm

My mom spent the next two weeks with me. At 82, she is remarkably vibrant, smart, and energetic and she is fantastic company. We always travel well together. I intended to stay busy with work, visiting customers for as long as possible. So, we embarked on weeklong road trip through Merritt, Kamloops,

Salmon Arm, Revelstoke, and Kelowna, B.C. It was great to have her with me at such a crucial time.

During our trip, we stayed at Airbnb's and enjoyed meals out. While I was in meetings, she explored the local areas. She's awesomely independent and had no trouble exploring on her own.

On our way to Revelstoke, I received a phone call from BC Cancer, notifying me that there was an opening for a PET scan the following week in Kelowna. I agreed to take the appointment, and they told me that they would cover the transportation, accommodation, and associated food costs. I thought, "Wow, amazing!"

Four generations of Cain's - *Warmed my heart.*

We had a great time in Revelstoke visiting with Aidan, Linda, and the kids. As luck would have it, Lauren was there at the same time, which was perfect. We had a big chunk of our family together. It was beyond awesome to have four generations of family together at this time. We were just missing my dad and Niall.

> ***"Love is the answer, at least for most of the questions in my heart."***
> — Jack Johnson, *"Better Together"*

The PET Scan

After visiting a few Hitfar customers in Vernon and Kelowna we arrived at the hospital at 1:50 PM. We waited about 30 minutes before they took me in. Not bad at all, I thought.

I wasn't sure how a PET Scan differs from a CT Scan so I did some research.

<u>*FUNCTIONALITY:*</u>

- **PET Scan**: Focuses on metabolic activity and function of cells. It can detect changes in cellular activity before structural changes occur.
- **CT Scan:** Focuses on anatomical structure and provides high-resolution images of physical structures.

<u>*Use of Contrast Material:*</u>

- **PET Scan:** Typically uses a radioactive tracer; no traditional contrast material is used.
- **CT Scan:** May use a contrast dye (either orally or intravenously) to enhance the visibility of certain areas, such as blood vessels or organs.

<u>*Radiation Exposure:*</u>

- **PET Scan:** Involves exposure to radioactive substances, but the levels are generally low and considered safe for diagnostic purposes.
- **CT Scan:** Involves exposure to ionizing radiation from X-rays, which can be higher than that of a PET scan, depending on the specific scan.

<u>*Time Required:*</u>

- **PET Scan:** Typically takes longer, often around 30 minutes to 2 hours, including preparation and waiting for the tracer to distribute.
- **CT Scan:** 10 minutes.

This procedure pretty much kicked everything into high gear with what happened next.

The following day a PORT-A-CATH was implanted in my chest at Royal Columbian Hospital in New Westminster. The surgery was easy. I was in and out of the hospital in about five hours. I was mildly sedated and conscious during the procedure. It was basically quick and painless.

G**OING** *Public with the Diagnosis*

After the port implant surgery, I made the decision to announce my cancer diagnosis on social media. By this point in the process, I felt it was time to share the news. This would prove to be one of the best choices I made throughout my entire cancer journey.

. . .

An Outpouring of Public Support

The response to my announcement was overwhelming with wave after wave of support coming in. Almost immediately, I felt the impact of my choice as hundreds of people rallied in my corner, sending messages of love and encouragement. Friends, family, and hundreds of acquaintances from years past reached out, offering their prayers and thoughts. I was particularly touched by messages from people I hadn't spoken to in over 30 years. My heart was overwhelmed by the number of connections that had endured despite time and distance apart.

Bob Cain
Mar 22

Guess if Princess Kate officially announced she has cancer today, so can I.

Yep, no joke. I was diagnosed with stage 3 colon cancer seven weeks ago. I've been very blessed to spend a bunch of time with family and close friends recently as I prepare myself physically an... See more

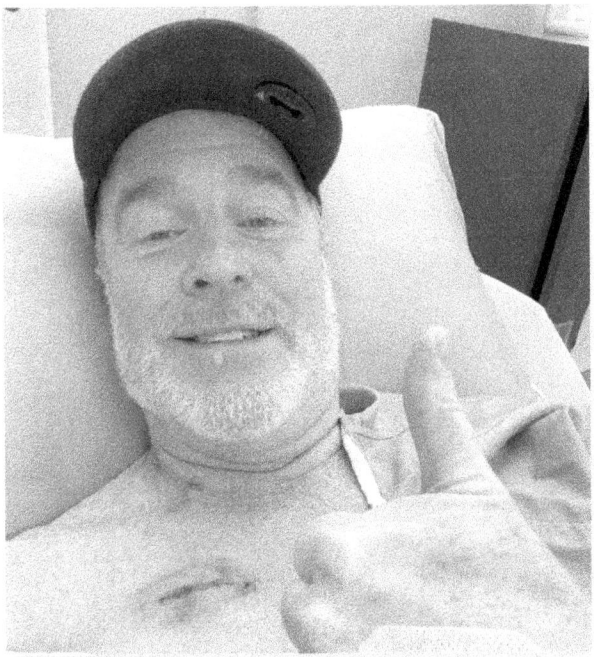

The Official Public Announcement *What turned out to be the single greatest game-changer of my entire cancer battle. I had no idea that an army of 350 people I'd met over the years would respond with overwhelming love and support for the next 16 months.*

The positive feedback was heartwarming and life-affirming. As I read the messages, I felt more hope and strength than at any other time in life. The words of encouragement reminded me that I was not alone in this battle. Each message was a source of comfort, further bolstering my resolve.

From that moment forward, I had an army of supporters cheering me on. My social network became a crucial part of my journey, providing immense emotional support and motivation as I prepared for the challenges ahead. Knowing that so many people cared about me and were rooting for my recovery helped me tremendously. The support I received empowered me. I can't possibly overstate how huge this aspect was for me. I would encourage anyone going through a challenging health crisis to do the same.

Social Waves

Going public with my diagnosis wasn't a marketing decision—it was a survival strategy. I needed connection. I needed love. And I needed to reclaim the narrative before fear swallowed me whole.

What I didn't fully realize at the time was that this would spark a phenomenon—one that would carry me through every stage of this journey. With every post, every update, every moment of vulnerability shared online, a ripple would begin. And from that a collective ripple would arise.

I've come to call these moments: **Social Waves**.

They are far more than social media posts. They are collective outpourings of energy—waves of love, strength, humour, empathy, and focused intention—launched into the world and returned to me a hundredfold. They were real-time exchanges between my spirit and the people who chose to ride this storm with me.

Each post became a portal for connection. A lifeline. And, as I came to believe more deeply, a form of healing in itself.

Throughout this book, you'll see these **Social Waves** visually separated from the main narrative. They're more than journal entries or public statements—they're snapshots of the energetic exchange that helped carry me through the hardest days of my life. They form the emotional and spiritual heartbeat of *24HrDay*.

First Surgery Consultation with Dr. MacNeill

March 28, 2024 - Dr. MacNeill advised that the PET Scan confirmed the cancer was stage 4. We were told it was stage 3 before that point. This meeting provided clarity on the aggressive nature of the treatment I would undergo, and the surgical procedures involved.

Surgical Procedure Details

Following the completion of chemotherapy, I'd have 6–8 weeks to recover before the next phase. First, I'd undergo an investigative laparoscopy—a minimally invasive procedure where a camera is inserted through small incisions in the abdomen. The goal was to get a direct view of the cancer's spread and confirm whether the planned surgery was still viable.

If all went as expected, I'd move on to Cytoreductive/HIPEC surgery. This would involve the removal of:

- **The affected section of my colon**
- **Lymph nodes**
- **Connected arteries**
- **Omentum**

After that, my entire abdominal cavity would be bathed in heated chemotherapy—HIPEC (Heated Intraperitoneal Chemotherapy). The idea was to kill off any remaining microscopic cancer cells directly at the source on contact.

Recovery Expectations

Recovery typically takes 3 to 6 months following this surgery. The last thing to recover is energy and strength. I got the sense that the surgery was going to be hardest part of the treatment plan and that it would most certainly kick my ass.

The consultation provided me with my first real understanding of the aggressive treatment plan. I felt that while chemotherapy would be challenging, it would also be the easiest part of the process. I was mostly concerned about the surgery itself. The thought of having my abdomen opened and my organs exposed terrified me. I chose not to dwell on it too much in the lead-up to the surgery. I told myself to take it one day at a time, one chemotherapy session at a time, one bloodwork session, and one CT scan at a time. I reassured myself that I would eventually get through this.

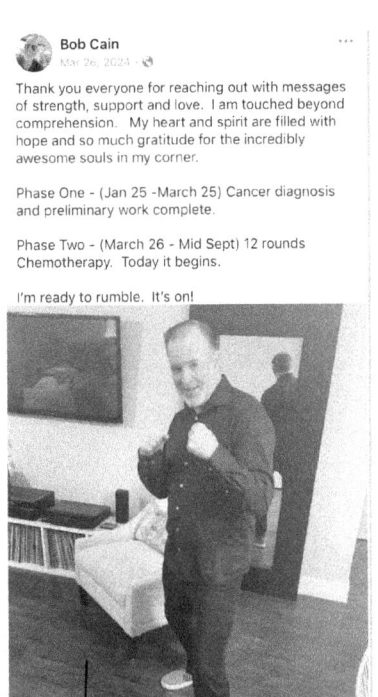

Go Time.

CHAPTER 4

CHEMOTHERAPY

"No dress rehearsal, this is our life."
— Tragically Hip, *"Ahead by a Century"*

Entering the Battle: Chemotherapy

After completing the first chemotherapy session, I was sent home with an infuser bottle to continue administering chemotherapy drugs over the next 46 hours. Along with the infuser, I was prescribed two additional medications:

Dexamethasone (Additional 4 Doses)

Purpose: In this context, the additional dose of dexamethasone serves multiple roles:

Anti-nausea: As mentioned earlier, it helps prevent nausea and vomiting associated with chemotherapy.

Anti-inflammatory: It helps manage inflammation

and can alleviate any immune response triggered by the chemotherapy drugs.

Appetite Stimulant: Can sometimes help stimulate appetite in patients undergoing treatment.

Metoclopramide

Purpose: Metoclopramide is prescribed to combat nausea and vomiting.

How It Works: Increases gastrointestinal motility, which helps move food through the stomach and intestines more quickly. This action can help reduce feelings of nausea.

The First 46-Hour Infuser: Post-Chemo at Home

After the infuser bottle was removed two days later, I had a recovery period of 12 days before my next round of chemotherapy. This recovery time is crucial, as it allows the body to heal and regain strength after the treatment.

I experienced some mild side effects including:

Canker Sores on the Tongue

Cause: Canker sores are often a result of chemotherapy, as these drugs can affect the mucous membranes in the mouth. Maintaining good oral hygiene and possibly using prescription mouth rinses can help manage this side effect.

Intermittent Hiccups

Cause: Hiccups can occasionally result from dexamethasone. While they may seem minor, they were uncomfortable and annoying.

My first round of chemotherapy went relatively smoothly, which was very encouraging. I was able to exercise most days and generally felt well. I was relieved to have completed this round, and now the countdown was on: one down, eleven more to go.

Family on the Move: Canadian Cancer Society Fundraiser

On April 1st, 2024, my three children and their partners joined a month-long fundraiser organized by the Canadian Cancer Society. The challenge involved walking or running a total of 80 kms throughout the month of April. The initiative coincided perfectly with the beginning of my chemotherapy treatments, making it a significant moment for our family. It essentially marked the beginning of the treatment plan for me. It was go time, and I was truly touched by their sentiment and everyone coming together to show their support.

Inspired by my children's commitment, my mom, great buddy Sean Lavoy, and I also joined the challenge. Walking 80 kms was ambitious, especially as I was starting chemotherapy, but I was determined to take part. By the end of April, every single one of us achieved our goal of walking or running 80 kms. Together, we covered a total of 792 kms and raised $1,562 for the Canadian Cancer Society.

A Birthday Commitment to Health

For my 52nd birthday, I made a significant purchase in line with my commitment to maintaining my health the best I could during my cancer journey. I purchased an Apple Ultra 2 fitness watch, viewing it not just as a gift, but as a tool to support my mission of staying active and engaged throughout my treatment and recovery.

Tracking Health Stats

I began to monitor my health regularly, especially in the context of the upcoming chemotherapy treatments and recovery period. Using the watch, I tracked key health statistics daily, including:

> ***Heart Rate:*** Monitoring my heart rate would help me gauge my cardiovascular health and ensure I was exercising regularly.
>
> ***Activity Levels:*** The watch would track my daily steps, workouts, and overall activity levels, providing insights into how active I was performing throughout treatment.
>
> ***Sleep Patterns:*** Understanding my sleep quality and duration would be crucial, as rest is vital for recovery and managing the side effects of chemotherapy.
>
> ***Calories Burned:*** Tracking calories burned would help me monitor my exercise regimen.

Commitment to Exercise

Tracking these stats was part of a larger commitment to exercise as much as possible during cancer treatment. I understood that physical activity would play a significant role in improving my overall well-being, boosting my energy levels, and potentially enhancing my response to treatment.

Setting Goals: With the watch, I set specific fitness goals for myself, whether it was aiming for a certain number of steps per day or completing a specific workout routine. This provided me with motivation and a sense of accomplishment.

Monitoring Progress: Collecting data over time allowed me to gain insights into my progress and helping me stay accountable to my plan.

Daily data collection was crucial for me to take ownership and accountability for the aspects of my health that I could control. Tracking my health statistics would not only motivate me to stay active but also provide valuable insights into my recovery process. With this tool, I embraced my cancer journey with a proactive mindset, focusing on maintaining both my physical and mental well-being every step of the way.

This was the evolution of my habitual practice of setting goals, monitoring, and tracking my progress. Everything that followed in my cancer battle strategy stemmed from those initial steps—A) buying the watch, and B) paying closer attention to my health statistics. I didn't realize it at the time, but this process laid the foundation for the 24HrDay philosophy and the program on which this book is based.

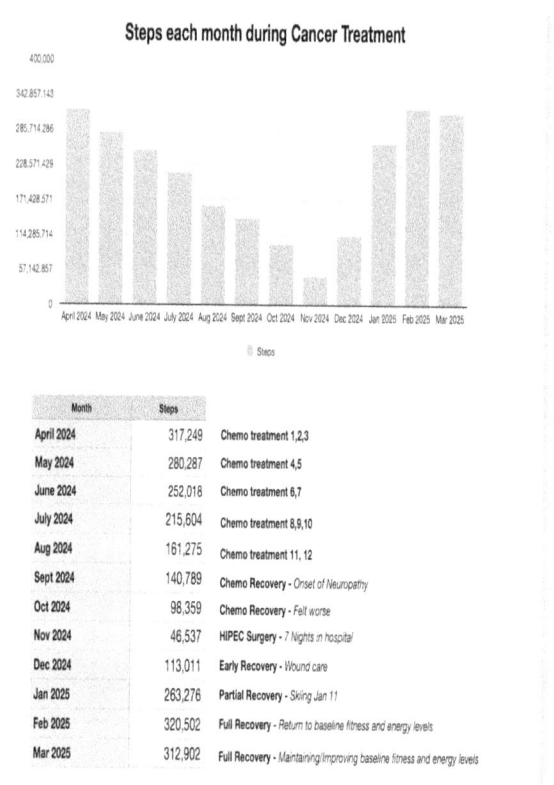

The Steady Decline and Rise *A visual arc of my journey —energy and mobility fading through chemo, then slowly rising again three weeks post-surgery and continuing into full recovery.*

The chart above illustrates collected data from my watch starting from the onset of my chemotherapy sessions and continuing until I was fully recovered one year later. It was clear that my energy and fitness steadily declined from the beginning of chemotherapy until about a month after my Cytoreductive/HIPEC surgery in November. By February 2025, my activity levels and energy had fully returned to baseline.

. . .

The Chemo Routine: *A Bi-Weekly Rhythm*
Chemo Treatment Day (Tuesday):

- Chemotherapy sessions happened every other Tuesday for 24 weeks. I spent roughly 4.5 hours in the chemotherapy chair at the hospital.
- Following this, I would have 46 hours of chemotherapy delivered via the infusion device attached to me while at home.

IV Removal (Thursday):

- Two days after chemo treatment, I would return to the hospital to have the infusion device removed from the PORT-A-CATH. This procedure is relatively simple, and I was trained to do it myself at home after the first two sessions.

Blood Work (Every Other Monday):

- The day prior to each treatment, I would visit the hospital lab for blood work. This was done to monitor my health and ensure my blood counts were within acceptable ranges before starting the next chemo cycle.
- Blood tests help assess the body's response to treatment, checking for any potential side effects, such as decreases in white blood cells, platelets, or other important health markers.

. . .

Humour as Medicine: ***Creative Social Media Posts and Lightheartedness***

Recognizing the challenges of undergoing chemotherapy, I adopted a fun and humorous approach to document my experience on social media. Before each chemotherapy session, I crafted a humorous social media post to keep my friends and family updated on my progress.

Maintaining a positive mindset was crucial not only for my own mental health but also for those around me. Staying open and light-hearted, I aimed to create an atmosphere of fun and positivity that could uplift both myself and my community.

Bobby Superfly Snooka!

Ride the Red Rooster!

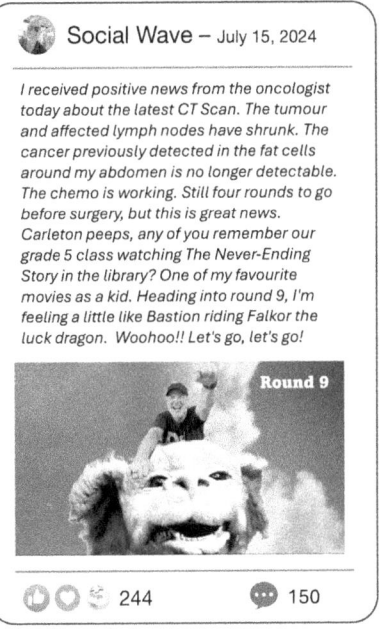

The Neverending Story - one of my favourite childhood movies. We must keep the story going.

I knew it would be a long road, but life is short, and we must enjoy it as much as possible for as long as we can. My friends and family appreciated my positive outlook. The humour helped create a supportive environment, allowing others to engage with my journey in a meaningful way. Making light of my situation provided me with a sense of relief. It shifted my focus away from the fear and difficulty of treatment, enabling me to cope with the emotional challenges I was experiencing.

Laughter can be a very powerful tool for battling a life-threatening disease.

Journal Entry #1 – The Fight for Life

Fighting for the right to live, love, and laugh longer is a universal struggle we all face daily. My cancer diagnosis, while initially devastating, has turned into a blessing in disguise, illuminating just how precious our time on this earth truly is. This experience has prompted me to adopt a new perspective on life—one that emphasizes gratitude, positivity, and connection.

A pivotal aspect of my journey will be my ongoing commitment to eliminating negative thoughts and behaviours. I acknowledge that while this is no easy task, it will be instrumental in navigating the challenges of cancer treatment. I will consciously remove feelings of concern, worry, fear, anxiety, and depression from my mind. These emotions serve no purpose other than to harm my physical, mental, and spiritual well-being.

I recognize that facing these challenges is difficult, but I also see it as the most rewarding experience of my life. I am gaining invaluable insights about myself and what it truly means to live, laugh, and love more deeply than ever before.

My cancer journey is a microcosm of life itself. The lessons I am learning will not only serve me well throughout my treatment but will also continue to benefit me for many years to come. My personal growth comes through adversity, and I will embrace whatever life throws my way.

I will approach life with determination and resilience, making the most of each day. I will cherish moments of joy and connection with my loved ones. I will improve my diet and stay as active as possible for as long as I can. I will practice mindfulness more regularly to gain better control over my thoughts and emotions. Through this practice, I will cultivate a greater sense of peace, harmony, and clarity in my life.

I will beat cancer, and in the process, I will become a better version of myself.

Side Effects: ***The First Two Rounds***

As I progressed through the first two rounds of chemotherapy I started to experience the following side effects.

Oral and Tongue Discomfort

Mouth Sores: These were notably worse but became more manageable by the end of the two-week period.

Sore Tongue: I experienced soreness on my tongue during the second week. My tongue felt burnt, like the sensation of having eaten something hot.

Hiccups and Remedies

Hiccups: I had hiccups after each chemotherapy session. This occurred for two days after each of the first two treatment cycles. I found that a simple remedy of lemon and sugar was somewhat effective in alleviating them. - Thank you, Linda Cain!

Skin Sensitivities

Acne: I got acne on my neck and the back of my head, which could be attributed to hormonal changes or reactions to the chemotherapy drugs.

Cold Sensitivity: I experienced heightened sensitivity to cold, which was uncomfortable but manageable. I couldn't drink cold drinks or touch ice.

Abdominal Discomfort

Cramps: I had intermittent cramps or a stitch-like sensation in the lower right side of my abdomen.

Sleep Patterns

Insomnia: The first week of chemotherapy was marked by insomnia. I noted an improvement in sleep quality during the second week.

Gastrointestinal Issues

Vomiting and Diarrhea: On day 8, I experienced vomiting and diarrhea twice, followed by another episode of diarrhea on day 9. The diarrhea came on suddenly while I was exercising. By suddenly I mean about 30 seconds to get to a toilet.

Appetite and Energy Levels

Strong Appetite: Throughout treatment, I maintained a strong appetite, which was encouraging. I made sure to eat nutritious foods to support my health and energy levels.

Overall Energy: Remarkably, I felt energetic and well for the most part, despite the side effects. I did not experience mental fog; instead, I felt positive, sharp, and focused.

Round Three: A Pattern Emerges
Hiccups

Severe hiccups for the first 52 hours after the chemotherapy session. This was particularly uncomfortable and disruptive during the initial phase of treatment.

IV Port Removal

I had no issues removing the IV from my PORT-A-CATH, which was a relief. The training I received on how to manage the device proved beneficial.

Exhaustion on Day 3

By day three, I was totally exhausted and had to lay down for most of the day. I was mostly inactive, standing only five times. I was definitely feeling the fatigue the doctors warned me to expect.

Gradual Recovery

Day 4: I felt about 75% of my usual energy but was able to work, albeit with reduced capacity.

Day 5: My energy increased to 90%, allowing me to return to exercising.

Day 6: I felt fully recovered, achieving 100% energy levels.

Oral Health Management

I managed to keep mouth sores at bay with the use of BC Cancer Magic Mouthwash, which helped maintain comfort during treatment. This became a staple for the rest of my chemotherapy treatments.

Diarrhea

On Day 8, I felt great but experienced a significant episode of diarrhea, which occurred twice until I felt completely empty. Notably, this episode happened exactly two weeks to the day and time from my previous similar experience. It seemed like a consistent pattern was emerging, as this issue occurred at the same time during each of the first three cycles.

Appetite and Activity Level

My appetite remained strong throughout the treatment, which was encouraging and helped me to maintain my energy levels.

Day 9, I played 18 holes of golf without any issues. I did not experience any bowel movements.

Day 10, the same situation persisted; I still hadn't had a bowel movement. I was experiencing occasional level one cramps when breathing deeply or lying on my right side.

CHAPTER 5

CANCER SAVED MY LIFE

"It's not the end / It's high time to wake up your mind."
— *Arcade Fire, Wake Up* (2004)

THE AWAKENING

In April, I came to an unexpected realization: the cancer diagnosis was somehow the best thing that could have happened to me. Before my diagnosis, my life had veered off course. I had lost sight of what mattered. I felt uninspired and disappointed as I entered my early 50s. I believed I was past my prime and hadn't come close to reaching my potential. I felt lost and lacked a clear course of direction.

I was really struggling with what to do with my life and the direction to head next. It was during this challenging time that I received my cancer diagnosis. I found myself at a crossroads. I could either turn my life around and make the most of the time I had left, or I could succumb to cancer. For me, the choice was clear: I wanted to live. I wanted another chance to fulfill my potential, strengthen my relationships and build the life of my dreams.

I decided to view my cancer diagnosis as a catalyst for personal development. For the first time in 35 years, I was completely sober. Suddenly, my life felt clearer. I began telling myself, "This cancer diagnosis is saving my life. I will have a much better life in the long run as a result." I must survive this.

April turned out to be much better than I thought. I expected chemotherapy to kick my ass. I prepared myself for the worst, but the reality wasn't as bad as I thought. I managed to walk or hike 160 kilometres in April which was more exercise in a month than I've done in my entire life. My determination was strong, and I felt good.

Before I knew it, May arrived, bringing nicer weather. I was excited to get back on the water with the SUPDOCK and go camping. D'Arcy was out of province, so I had a few days to myself. I was between chemo treatments and feeling pretty good. Eager to enjoy the outdoors, I planned a solo overnight camping trip.

Solo Voyage to Twin Islands

I packed my camping gear: a tent, two small tables, a chair, a Coleman stove, and healthy food & drinks in a cooler. It wasn't a lot, but it was enough for one night. I drove to Belcarra Provincial Park, parked the car, and wheeled my gear down to the beach. I inflated the dock, attached the motor, and loaded everything onto it before setting off by myself up Indian Arm toward Twin

Islands. There are about 20 camping spots on Big Twin Island available on a first-come, first-served basis for kayakers and boaters.

It was a beautiful, sunny day, and I felt exhilarated to be on the water with the SUPDOCK. Many onlookers asked where I got it and where they could buy one. I told them I made it and planned to sell them soon on supdock.ca. I was proud of myself for attempting an overnight camping trip completely solo. It was time for me to reconnect with nature, take it all in, and fill my soul with the beauty of Indian Arm.

The thing I remember most about that trip was waking up to the chorus of birds chirping and singing above me. So many different calls, all weaving together in the canopy overhead. Two eagles soared nearby, going through their morning routine. The sky was just beginning to glow with a soft blue hue, and the air was completely still.

When I looked out at the water, it was like glass. *Oh my goodness,* I thought. *I've never seen Indian Arm this calm.*

I crawled out of the tent and wandered over to my chair at the edge of the ridge, my bare feet sinking into the thick, soft carpet of moss. *Oh, this is nice.*

Out on the water, I spotted three harbour seals with their heads up, just floating and listening, rolling lazily in the silence. No boats. No sounds of human activity. Just birdsong and the quiet rhythm of nature.

Pure happiness.

One of the most peaceful, beautiful moments I've ever felt.

The Main Journal **Begins**

Midway through May, I began to feel real benefits from the

lifestyle changes I had made. I felt fitter and healthier, with a clear mind free from negative cumbersome thoughts. I was consistently present and happy in the moment. My relationships were stronger than ever, and my path forward was clear. I focused on my health and the strength of my relationships to beat cancer and make a full recovery.

At this point, I began to keep a more detailed account of my thoughts and experiences. I started what became "The Main Journal" of my battle with cancer. I documented as much of my cancer journey as possible in order to write a book about my experience navigating the Canadian healthcare system while battling and overcoming cancer.

The reward for beating cancer, beyond extending my life, would be the opportunity to write a book that could hopefully help others in similar situations do the same.

The following section of the book features my personal journal entries from the months that followed, interwoven with social media posts that capture my experiences in real time. These entries provide a candid look at my journey while I navigated the ups and downs of treatment, recovery, and self-discovery.

While journalling, I documented my thoughts, feelings, and reflections in order to offer an intimate glimpse into my mindset during this time. Each entry serves as a snapshot of my emotional state, detailing not only the physical challenges I faced but also the mental and emotional hurdles I encountered along the way.

My social media posts, on the other hand, reflect my desire to share my experiences while seeking support from my community. They capture moments of vulnerability, triumph, and everything in between, showcasing how I processed each day during treatment.

. . .

Journal Entry #1 – Living by Design

Each day is a gift. Do what I can, while I can. Dream big and pursue those dreams with focus and determination. I have one life to live, so I'll give it my all. How I spend my time—where and with whom—shapes my health, happiness, and success. I will choose my purpose, path, and people wisely.

I am building healthy habits and routines that are realistic given my energy and capacity. Consistency is the aim. This journey is about living fully while improving my physical and mental well-being.

I will nurture stronger relationships through compassion and understanding. Fear, worry, and anxiety drain joy—so I'll work to manage those emotions and keep positivity front and centre. This journal is about cultivating joy and resilience over the long haul.

Lasting happiness isn't about fleeting highs—it's built through daily habits and thought patterns. I will create a consistent, positive mental attitude. Over time, this mindset will shape my evolution into the best version of myself.

I want to be a better writer, so I'll write. A better singer, so I'll sing. A better producer, so I'll create. I'll stretch, move, meditate, and nourish my body with healthier food. I'll reduce distractions—news, social media, and mindless scrolling—and replace them with intention.

I'll be more present and pay attention to those around me. I'll care for myself with more consistent hygiene and invest in meaningful relationships. I'll stay in touch with loved ones and take pride in maintaining my home, car, and the things I've worked hard for.

Set goals. Make a plan. Execute. Measure. Adjust. Repeat. I'll refine my systems and learn to maximize time. This is my design. I have 24 hours each day to move my dreams into reality.

And through it all, I'll travel with love in my heart and compassion in my soul—welcoming and kind to everyone I meet.

May 28 – The Sobriety Shift

I'm halfway through round five of chemotherapy. This is the first time I didn't create a funny post for social media, and also the first round where recovery took a full four days. Earlier rounds only needed one or two. On day eight, I was hit again with brutal diarrhea—multiple trips to the bathroom, emptying my system entirely, even spitting up yellow bile. It wasn't pleasant.

I'm choosing to spend time with people who encourage, understand, and challenge me. I'm learning to be unapologetically selfish with my dreams and to walk toward them with pride and purpose. With determination and a clear plan, I believe I can shape a life of my own design.

Sobriety is teaching me something I hadn't expected: deep satisfaction. Before my diagnosis, drinking felt like a reward for hard work—a way to unwind and feel free. But alcohol is a toxin. It damages brain cells, disrupts emotions, and leads to impulsivity and instability. It wrecked my patterns. Bad hangovers meant lost days, poor food choices, and spirals of depression and anxiety.

Now, sober for just a few months, I see healthy patterns forming. I used to need four full days without alcohol or weed to get back to a positive baseline—just in time to want to party again. Drinking 6–10 ounces of alcohol three to four times a week had started to feel normal. It wasn't. It was a sickness. A terrible cycle. I can't go back. That liquor store is bad news, Bob.

We're not born with bad habits; we collect them. The key is to identify, reinforce, and protect the good ones while eliminating the harmful ones—and the toxic people who encourage them. That kind of focus will carry me toward the life I want.

It's time to hang up my hang-ups—emotional baggage, grudges, self-righteousness, judgment. Letting go of these things frees me to grow and live with clarity. I'm setting my sights on a life of positive change. One day, one choice, one hour at a time—with love in my heart and a message to share: healing is possible.

June 2 – Behaviours in Focus

I'm becoming more intentional with my habits and routines, staying present and reflecting on how each action affects my mental, physical, and spiritual well-being. These daily behaviours are building blocks—designed to bring me closer to the person I want to become.

Turning goals into habits is how I'll transform my life. The key is focusing on what truly matters and consistently aligning my actions with that vision.

This same intentionality applies to my relationships—especially with D'Arcy, Mom, Dad, my kids, and my grandkids. Presence, purpose, and love must guide how I show up.

"Oh, I'm a lucky man / To count on both hands / The ones I love…"
— *Eddie Vedder, "Just Breathe"*

June 5 – A Wake-Up Call

Today I'm heading to Niagara for Mom's birthday. I can't wait to be surrounded by family and friends—I want to make the most of every moment. One of my buddies Jamie Hodges has arranged to get 16 of my lifelong friends together for a golf tournament to support me in me cancer battle. I'm really excited to see everyone and super touched by the gesture. Thank you so much Jamie.

Last night, I barely slept. My mind raced, likely from the dexamethasone. Around 4 AM, I began questioning the life I was living before my diagnosis. Was I drifting toward self-destruction, mistaking indulgence for happiness? Why hadn't I achieved the goals I held for so long? Was I truly showing up as the son, partner, father, and friend I wanted to be?

I've realized how much work there is to do. And I'm ready.

I will beat cancer—and I will rebuild my life with purpose. Through intention, discipline, and consistent habits, I will become who I've always known I could be. I won't back down. I will complete myself.

June 6 – Mom's 81st Birthday

We planned a beautiful day to celebrate my mom's 81st birthday—a day that turned out to be more meaningful than we could have anticipated.

We started with a quiet breakfast together before heading into St. Catharines to pick up my dad from Linhaven, his long-term care residence. From there, we drove south along Lakeshore Road, the shoreline of Lake Ontario guiding us into Niagara-on-the-Lake. My dad used to teach Grade 5 at Parliament Oak School there—a building filled with history and memories. In fact, he taught Shannon in both Grade 3 and Grade 5.

We picked up Lauren in town, and the four of us continued along the scenic Niagara Parkway toward Niagara Falls. We stopped briefly at Queenston Heights, the historic site where Canadian forces held off the Americans during the War of 1812—preserving our independence. The symbolism wasn't lost on me. Every time I hear ridiculous comments about Canada becoming the "51st state," I laugh. We've got our flaws, sure—but Canada is strong and free, and we're not signing up for that circus across the border anytime soon.

But I digress.

By the time we reached Niagara Falls, Dad was tired and ready to head back. We returned him to Linhaven, and while the visit was short, it was special. It meant the world to Mom to have us all together for her birthday.

That evening, we capped it off with an incredible dinner at Weinkeller in Niagara Falls. Big thanks to Jules—an old friend from the Henley high school days—who took amazing care of us. She hooked us up with a memorable experience and helped make the night even more special.

It was one of those rare, simple days that holds everything: love, memory, aging, history, family, gratitude. A good day. A great day.

Happy 81st birthday Mom!

June 7 – Eyes Forward

I'm in the fight of my life—and I'm ready. I've set my goals, prioritized them, and I'm taking action every day. I hold myself fully accountable. I'm here to love harder, express my gratitude openly, and make each moment count.

I'm not done. I am nowhere near ready to die. I have the strength and will to survive this. Pain and suffering will come, but I will endure. What matters is how I respond when it hits—how I breathe through it, cope, and keep going.

One day at a time. One step. One breath. Just keep moving.

I've faced my despair and named it.
I'm clear on what must change—and I own all of it. The greatest challenges carry the greatest potential for growth. The problem is never the obstacle—it's how we choose to see it. Every hardship is a teacher; the harder the lesson, the deeper the transformation.

We are all the product of our own design.

I choose forgiveness over resentment.

I choose presence over regret.

I choose love.

The past doesn't define me.

What I do today does.

Virtue will guide how I fight this battle.

Right now, in 2024, the answer is clear: beat cancer. Stay focused. Live my truth. Survive.

DOWNPOURS, Brotherhood and Birdies

Jamie Hodges' remarkable gift of support—a golf tournament at Rockway Vineyards. Sixteen of my closest friends from St. Catharines showed up. These were the guys I grew up playing sports with, men who had stood by me through various chapters of life. Our broader friend group back home might stretch 80 people wide, but this was a hand-picked crew—a tight circle of good-time boys who've shared decades of laughs, stories, and support. Among them was my son Niall, and his best friend Jack making the day even more meaningful.

The day was nothing short of magic. We were blessed with a bit of everything—sunshine, downpours, an electric mix of weather that somehow mirrored the full spectrum of life. There was laughter, high fives and hugs—old stories retold, and a deep, unspoken bond between lifelong buddies. Each of these men made it unmistakably clear they were with me, behind me, and ready to carry me through this fight. Seeing them all gathered in one place, united in purpose and presence, was one of the most profoundly touching and heartwarming experiences of my life.

Social Wave – Jun 9, 2024

Awesome day with this crew of lifelong buddies. A lot of us have known each other for 35+ years. We played through four different rounds of rain and thunderstorms mixed with crazy winds, sun and clouds. We played through every type of sideways weather you could imagine.
It was hilarious and super fun. I'm touched by the amount of love and support I received today from all you guys. Thank you all for coming out today and playing through the elements. The friendship, encouragement and brotherly love I felt today filled me with the strength of an army. Special thanks to Jamie Hodges for organizing this event. Much appreciated. You're the best.

   205   34

The icing on the cake? Niall ended up winning the tournament.

Bob and Niall

Golf is Niall's passion. It's where he finds his joy and his flow. To watch him not only be there by my side but also play his heart out and win among my lifelong friends—well, that was pure poetry. And our relationship? It has blossomed into something truly special over these past few years. We're more than father and son now—we're buddies, teammates, and spiritual companions. Niall has always carried a quiet wisdom and calm energy, like a natural-born Buddha. He's insightful, centred, and deeply kind.

Whenever I'm in town, he drops everything to be with me. Whether we're golfing, grabbing food, or watching a movie, his presence is a gift. We have rich, philosophical conversations and share a comfort and closeness that I treasure deeply. That day on the course wasn't just about golf. It was about love, connection, and the kind of support that carries a man through the storm.

June 10 – Remembering My Father

We visited my dad today. He's been in long-term care with frontotemporal dementia for the past five years—a terrible disease that slowly and brutally strips away a person's personality, empathy, and awareness. While he's still alive, the man we knew has been gone for a long time. None of us know how much time is left, but today I'm reflecting on the incredible father, husband, and friend he was throughout his life.

My Dad, Brian and me.

My dad was unwavering in his love and commitment to our family. He had a deep passion for sports—football, hockey, golf, curling, skiing, and cards—and a love for travel that took him to over 70 countries, often organizing trips for groups of friends. He was a natural teacher and mentor, coaching kids' sports and even teaching my ex-wife Shannon in elementary school. So many of my friends were shaped by his steady presence and playful encouragement.

He supported me through some of the most difficult chapters of my life. As a role model, he never spoke ill of anyone and always lived with integrity and joy. He loved to laugh and made it a point to live life on his own terms. As a husband, he was unshakable and supportive of my mom, encouraging her education and career every step of the way. He was a true partner.

He was also a progressive man—never a trace of bigotry or chauvinism in his words. He was kind, loving, and full of life, and he passed those values on to me, my brother, and his grandchildren.

It's heartbreaking that frontotemporal dementia took so much from him—and from us. The disease gradually erased the vibrant, generous, and gentle man we knew. It made him difficult to be around in the later years, but that was never who he truly was. We choose to remember the version of him we knew for most of our lives: joyful, thoughtful, devoted, and loving.

We were lucky to have him. And we will never forget him.

June 26 – Listening to My Body

I've slept more over the past four nights than I have in months, and it's made a real difference. I'm feeling pretty good—about 85% energy. I'm still a bit slow and tired, but it's manageable. Tonight, I'm meeting D'Arcy after work for the Cage the Elephant and Young the Giant show.

I've got just two days left at Hitfar. I've worked as long as I can, and now it's time to step away and focus entirely on recovery. I'll be off work until I've fully recovered from surgery—likely six to nine months from now, if all goes according to plan.

It's time to go all in on my health and well-being. I'm committed to finishing this treatment plan strong. I have a CT scan scheduled for Saturday, and next week I'll find out how things are progressing. At this point in the journey, I feel as good as I could possibly hope. Now it's about staying consistent and getting even more focused with my activity and recovery goals.

The concert tonight was amazing—Young the Giant and Cage the Elephant both put on incredible shows. The energy in the crowd was electric. It felt good to be alive.

JUNE 27 - REST When Needed

I woke up feeling tired and decided sent D'Arcy to work with the car. I stayed in bed until 9:30, got up to make breakfast, then found myself back on the couch until 2 PM. I'm really feeling the fatigue today, and "chemo mouth" has kicked in hard—my lips are sore, and there's a lingering metallic taste I can't shake.

I'm trying to check off some of my daily habits, but some days are just harder than others. I still want to make the effort, even if I'm not at full strength. At the same time, it's important to rest when my body is clearly asking for it. I've been pushing hard the past few days, and the chemo is catching up with me.

Overall, I'm doing well. I just need to listen to my body and rest when needed. There's no reason to stress—just do my best.

JULY 3 - Momentum Returns

Great day! I bounced back strong—cleaned the house and

yard and tripled my exercise goal. I hiked, biked, played tennis, and even got in a round of disc golf. I ate clean, stretched, meditated, and played some music before getting to bed by 9:30.

Tomorrow morning is my CT scan. I'm hoping—and praying—for positive results. I need to know the treatment is working, that the cancer is receding. Aside from the usual day-two chemo hiccups (they still suck), I'm feeling remarkably well.

In a few days I'll drive to Salmon Arm to meet Aidan, Linda, and the kids at their provincial park campsite. I'm stoked to hit the water with the boys on our electric butt scooters. Feeling pure joy.

July 14–16 – Results and Resolve

After a rejuvenating trip to Salmon Arm, I returned Wednesday night and slept well. Thursday, I golfed—walked 9 km and shot an 89. I felt strong. But by Friday and Saturday, fatigue set in hard. I barely left the couch, mostly sleeping and resting. Sunday, I found a bit more strength and planned to ride my bike and catch live music in the park.

The momentum has been working. I reminded myself: don't let it slip. Recommit.

July 15 – CT Scan Results

Incredible news: the tumor in my colon and affected lymph nodes have shrunk. Even better—there's no longer visible cancer in the abdominal fat tissue. There are some abnormal fat cells around the liver that need checking, but the doctor isn't too concerned. I'll have an ultrasound soon to be safe.

On a less exciting note, a sharp pain in my gums turned out to be a tiny piece of bone pushing its way out—another chemo side effect, I guess. Brutal.

July 16 – Round #9: Final Third

I began round nine of chemo today. I'm in the final third of treatment, and the scan results give me confidence. I know I can finish this. But I've let a few commitments slip over the past two weeks. It's time to refocus.

I must control what I can control—starting with my thoughts and behaviours. Good intentions are one thing, but discipline and consistency are everything. Only I can hold myself accountable.

July 21 – Holding Steady

After a fun day in Whistler, I was hit hard again—48 hours down. Chemo mouth, vomiting, diarrhea, food tasting awful, dizziness when I stood. I slept for most of it. I just have to listen to my body and ride it out.

No matter what, Bob… stick to the plan.

July 30 – Progress and Pressure

I haven't written in a while, so here's the catch-up.

I started driving Uber again to cover rent, bills, and groceries. I've got no income right now, and I want to avoid building up debt. Driving for a few hours each day has helped—not just financially, but emotionally. I've had meaningful 20–30-minute conversations with strangers. It feels good to connect.

I met with Dr. MacNeill on Monday. She was thrilled with my progress. The chemo is working—the tumor and lymph nodes have shrunk significantly, and there's no cancer detected in the abdominal fat. It's huge news, and confirmation from a second opinion gives me even more confidence. Surgery is scheduled for September and October. She's even trying to schedule the laparoscopic procedure around the kids' visit for our Fam Jam.

Even with this progress, I'm still in the middle of it. But the confirmation that the treatment is working fuels my drive to keep building healthy routines—and deepen them. I've got zero stress in my relationships. I feel aligned with D'Arcy, my family, and even with the people I meet in passing.

With stage 4 cancer, life sharpens. Every choice counts. And I'm choosing to win.

Aug 4–10 – Desolation Sound

The last four days were rough. I slept and rested as much as possible to prepare my body for a seven-day trip to Desolation Sound, B.C.. This is a bucket list trip I've dreamed about for ten years, and super excited. I've planned and thought about this intensely over the last nine months. Everything related to SUPDOCK was aimed at making this trip as comfortable as possible. Well, here we are, ready to do it. Tonight, we're in a hotel in Gibsons, prepared to enter the wild at dawn. We have seven days to explore, and I feel well-rested and very excited.

Aug 7 - Salt Water, Sunshine and Stars

We are 48 hours into our adventure. We launched at noon Monday from Okeover Harbour Marina. It's $5 a night for parking, sweet deal. We are out here for seven days.

Day 1 - We set off on the motorized SUPDOCK, towing paddle boards with seven days of supplies. Spent the day sunning, swimming and cruising around Okeover Arm. We pulled into Grace Harbour campsite around 7:30 PM. There are only two camping pads at that site. They were both taken. Our only option was to set up a campsite on the top of a relatively flat rock, approximately 20x10 feet, about 40 feet off the beach. We were in the tidal zone, but it looked like the tide would not reach the top of the rock where we would be set up our camp for the night. At high tide, the water rose to within a foot of our makeshift spot. Close call, but we used the SUPDOCK as a camping pad on the rock. If the tide rose another 18 inches, we would have floated off with all our gear intact.

The only flat spot I could find as dusk settled was on this rock in the today zone.

It was a magical night—just the two of us, surrounded by salt water, watching the tides rise and fall nearly 14 feet in front of us.

The day had been full of marine life: shrimp, crab, starfish, jellyfish, sea urchins, and seals galore. As night fell, we pitched our tent with the fly off and drifted to sleep under a blanket of stars—millions of them.

We woke around 6 a.m. to the sun rising into a bright blue sky. The tide had receded nearly 100 feet, revealing the rocky beach below the giant rock we'd camped on. The transformation overnight was stunning. We were no longer surrounded by water—we were grounded again, quite literally.

Then, around 8 a.m., we got an unexpected wake-up call. Two park rangers arrived and kindly—yet firmly—evicted us from our little paradise. Apparently, camping outside the designated tent pads was strictly prohibited. One of them issued a citation and a warning, and I explained our situation honestly: the sun was setting, we didn't want to risk paddling farther in the dark, and we'd done our best to respect the space.

He gave a half-smile and said, "I get it... just don't get into any more trouble this week, or you'll be removed from the park."

"Yes, sir," I replied, grateful for the leniency. We packed up quickly, cleaned the site thoroughly, and paddled off—the water was dead calm. It was a beautiful morning. No harm, no foul.

Looking back, that night remains one of my proudest moments. It was spontaneous, bold, and beautiful. We were immersed in nature, completely unplugged and alive. Rule-bending aside, it was one of those rare moments where everything aligned—stars above, salt air, and a perfect reminder that life is for living.

DAY 2 - EXPLORED MORE of the shoreline of Okeover Arm to Hare Point campground. There are 18 tent pads here and only four of them were occupied last night. Managed to get a prime spot and set up the solar panels we need to recharge batteries for the motor and keep the fridge/freezer cooler cold enough for food and drinks. Day 3 - Woke up slow and made a nice breakfast. We are just chilling at this spot for the day. Seems like a good base camp. Heading out in the paddle boards soon. 48 hours in we are having a great time and feeling super relaxed, immersed in the beauty of Desolation Sound.

Hare Point. We had the west facing beach all to ourself for three days. Epic.

The Desolation Sound trip was an epic accomplishment—something I'd dreamed of doing ever since moving to B.C. in 2014. It had been on my bucket list for years. The fact that D'Arcy and I were able to pull it off together, using our newly invented SUPDOCK, made it even more meaningful. It was the realization of a dream.

Spending five nights and six days in the wilderness while battling stage 4 colon cancer gave me a profound sense of empowerment and pride. I was truly harnessing the power of the 24HrDay.

I slept the entire drive back to Vancouver with D'Arcy behind the wheel. Once home, we unpacked the car and got settled into our cozy space—and then I slept for five days straight. Looking back, I honestly don't know how I did it. I think it must have been adrenaline that carried me through Desolation Sound. Somehow, I pushed through. And damn, am I ever proud of that trip. It was incredible.

Social Wave – Aug 11, 2024

Made it home, safe and sound after six days (5 nights) at Desolation Sound. We're definitely exhausted, and a little sore. The trip was a tonne of fun but also a lot of work. A hot shower and cozy bed seem really nice right now. Happy to be back home ☺

A few people asked me about the SUP motors. They attach easily to the fin housing on the bottom of the SUP or dock. See photo. They could work on a canoe or kayak as well.

The battery box is strapped on top and the motor is controlled with a Bluetooth remote. Sit, stand, kneel, lay down, whatever you like....and cruise.

   77   6

Aug 17 – Almost There

It's so hard to fight when you feel weak. I feel like I'm constantly stuck in the throes of the chemo. My body feels sick and toxic. When I stand, I can feel the water in my body swoosh around. I feel dizzy and nauseous. This is terrible.

They told me the sides effects of the chemo would be cumulative over time, and they would get worse as I proceeded through all 12 rounds. I must admit I feel like absolute crap at this point. At least it's almost over. Only one more session to go.

The day I rang the bell at the end of chemo was paramount. This is a powerful and symbolic tradition in many cancer treatment centres. Its relevance lies in both personal meaning and collective ritual. Here's why it matters:

A Symbol of Completion and Triumph

Ringing the bell marks the end of a grueling treatment journey. For patients, it symbolizes survival, perseverance, and the strength it took to get through chemotherapy's physical and emotional toll. It's a moment of triumph—often hard-earned—and gives a sense of closure to a harrowing chapter.

A Public Acknowledgment

Chemo can feel isolating. Ringing the bell invites caregivers, fellow patients, and medical staff to witness the milestone. It turns a private struggle into a shared moment of celebration, validating the journey in a communal space.

A Beacon of Hope

For others still undergoing treatment, hearing that bell can be deeply motivating. It becomes a sound of hope—proof that the finish line is real and reachable. The ritual carries emotional weight, serving as both encouragement and inspiration.

An Emotional Release

The act provides an outlet for the flood of emotions that often follow the final treatment: relief, fear, joy, grief, exhaustion, and gratitude. It's a pause to honour everything endured.

Social Wave – Aug 27, 2024

After a long 5 months of chemotherapy, I finally rang the bells today. 12 rounds - DONE!

Feeling worn out, physically and emotionally drained, but very relieved to put this phase of the treatment plan in the rear view mirror and get back to feeling myself again.

Thanks first and foremost to D'Arcy for being at my side every step of the way. Every single day. And in every way possible. You have been amazing. Thank you BC Cancer for the top notch care and support. The doctors and nurses have all been amazing.

Thanks to my family for all the love and support. Stoked to see you all soon for a 10 day fam-jam between surgeries.

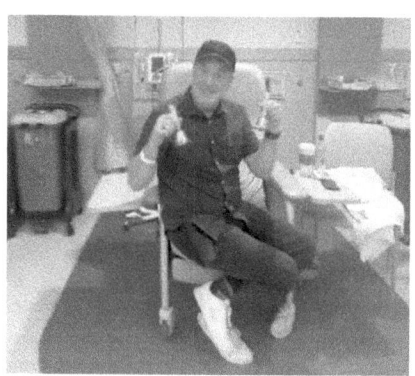

Lastly, thank you Facebook friends for the well wishes, massages and incredible support. It really means a lot. I'm so grateful to you.

Onward to phase 2 - two upcoming surgeries in Sept and Oct.

   256   119

Ringing there bells was a monumental moment. I shed a tear.

CHAPTER 6

POST-CHEMO RELIEF & REFOCUS

"There is a light and it never goes out."
— *The Smiths*

I was so happy to be done chemotherapy. I could hardly believe I had spent five straight months in a state of continuous physical decline—but I battled through, and I made it. Now, I had two months to regain my strength and prepare for what I imagined would be the hardest part of the battle: the HIPEC surgery.

The thought of having my abdomen opened from sternum to pelvis scared the shit out of me. Then came the image of surgeons combing through my insides, cutting and burning out as much cancer as they could find, followed by a heated chemotherapy rinse poured over all my internal organs. Yeah… that freaked me out. So, I reminded myself: **It's not happening today.** I still have a 24HrDay to make the most of. That's exactly how I chose to move forward.

Fam Jam 2024: Reconnection and Joy

I was especially excited for the upcoming 2024 Fam Jam—our annual gathering when Aidan, Linda, Niall, Rachel, Lauren, Oliver, Noah, and I all come together, usually for about ten days in B.C. This year, we planned to spend three days on Bowen Island followed by a full week in Revelstoke. I was thrilled that I didn't have any chemo sessions looming. I figured my strength would only grow as I worked my way back to full health before the November surgery.

CHAPTER 6 | 121

Bowan Island, Fam Jam kick off 2024

The trip felt perfectly timed—one final stretch of reconnection and joy before the next major phase of treatment. And as if that wasn't enough, I was stoked to spend a week with Danny Lawrence, a lifelong buddy from St. Catharines who was flying out to see me at the end of September. We've been through a lot together over the years—adventures, misadventures, music, loss, and laughter. Having Danny come out just to hang, share stories, and be present before I went under the knife meant more than I could put into words.

It all felt like the right kind of buildup: time with the people I love, in the places I love, surrounded by nature, humour, and a sense of forward motion. The calm before the storm—but this time, on my terms.

Lauren arrived Sept 4th, giving us a few days to hang out one-on-one before Niall and his girlfriend Rachel joined us. Once they arrived, we'd be heading straight to the ferry and over to our Airbnb on Bowen Island for three days of rest, beach time, and reconnection. Medicine for the soul.

Two Bears **on the Trail**

Lauren and I kicked off our time together with a four-hour hike to the first summit of Mount Seymour in North Vancouver. Funny story—while we were driving and chatting on the way to the mountain, Lauren said, "I hope we see some bears out there today, Daddy Bear Chair." I laughed and replied, "Yeah, that would be super cool, Lauren Bear."

Mt. Seymour Summit Hike

The bear pet names have been a thing between us since she was a little girl. She would always crawl up into my lap whenever I was sitting down and say, "Up, up, Daddy Bear Chair!" I started calling her Lauren Bear back then, and I guess we've both been bears ever since. She's 27 now, but her name in my phone is still "Lauren Bear."

Sure enough, about halfway up the trail, two black bears came bouncing out right in front of us—no more than 40 feet away! We laughed hysterically—"Yay, two bears!"—then cautiously made our way past them on the way to the summit.

Two Bears!

We followed that day up with a 8-hour SUP cruise up Indian Arm to Twin Islands. It was fantastic to connect with Lauren one on one after such a long summer.

My relationship with Lauren is something truly special. We've always had an amazing time together, whether it was our early trips to B.C. when she was younger or later adventures to New York City, Miami, and the Florida Keys—just the two of us. Maybe it's the classic father-daughter bond, but there's something even deeper there. As the youngest of my three children, Lauren has always had a sweet, loving nature—an old soul with remarkable empathy and emotional intelligence.

She's also my business partner in Eco-Train, leading all our marketing and graphic design efforts with creativity and dedication. I'm incredibly proud of her and love her to pieces. Despite living 5,000 kilometres apart, our bond has only grown stronger over time. Every visit feels epic—full of laughter, deep talks, and meaningful moments I cherish.

We had an absolute blast in Revelstoke after that, joining up with Aidan, Linda, and the kids. Most of our time was spent just hanging out and enjoying the mountain town vibe, but we also managed a one-night camping trip with Aidan's new trailer — a cozy little getaway.

One of the highlights was taking a cruise around Lake Revelstoke on the original prototype SUPDOCK, which I'd passed on to Aidan. All five of us piled on — even Mikha, Aidan's loyal Jindu husky, came along for the ride. It was classic. We capped the night off under a sky lit up by spectacular northern lights. Truly unforgettable.

Bob Cain is with **Lauren Cain** and **4 others.**
Sep 22 · 🌐

FAMJAM 24 is in the books. So awesome to spend the last few weeks with my kids and grand kids just having fun. We had a lot of laughs and experienced the northern lights which was a sweet bonus.

👍❤️ Anita Vinarterta and 91 others   14 comments

SUPDOCKing with Family. Northern Lights on full display—a magical first for most of us, pure magic under the stars.

Danny's First Trip to BC

A few days after the kids flew back to Ontario, my old friend Danny Lawrence arrived for his first-ever trip to British Columbia

—he'd never even been east of Manitoba. I was excited to show him around.

Though my energy was in steady decline, I pushed through to make sure he had the best time possible. We caught *Peter Hook and The Light* at the Commodore Ballroom, dancing to both *Substance* albums by Joy Division and New Order—pure nostalgic joy with a crowd of 50-somethings reliving the soundtrack of our youth.

We hiked, explored, and took the motorized paddle boats out for a spin. Danny had a great time—but afterward, I was set up for a month of exhaustion. Still worth it.

Bob, Danny and D'Arcy for the week.

Sept 6: Diagnostic Laparoscopy

One step closer to a brand-new lease on life.

They hadn't found any new or unexpected spread of cancer, at least not according to the imaging results available from the latest CT scan. But to get a clearer picture before deciding whether I was a candidate for HIPEC surgery, I underwent a diagnostic laparoscopy—a minimally invasive procedure designed to give the surgical team a direct view of the inside of my abdominal cavity.

Dr. Trevor Hamilton performed the laparoscopy at UBC Hospital in Vancouver. Under general anesthesia, he made three small incisions in my abdomen and inserted a fibre-optic camera to explore areas that imaging alone can't fully assess. It was a relatively short-day procedure, but the significance of it was massive: the laparoscopy allowed the team to assess the extent and distribution of visible peritoneal disease. This step was critical in determining whether cytoreductive surgery with HIPEC would be possible.

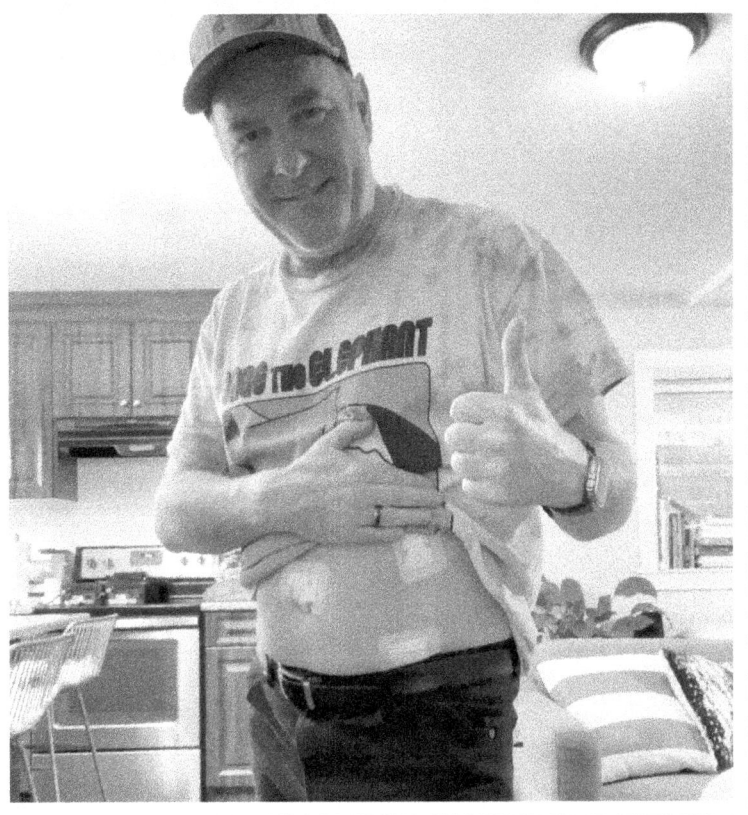

Laparoscopic Surgery *Things were looking good post-chemo—this was the next big step forward.*

The good news? There were no major surprises. No new lesions that ruled out surgery. Based on what they saw, the cancer appeared confined to discrete regions that could potentially be removed surgically.

This was the ultimate affirmation: the disease seemed manageable—and if all went well, it might be curable. I could see the path ahead. One where I might live, thrive, and reclaim my future. I am feeling alive and revived.

. . .

PERIPHERAL NEUROPATHY BEGINS

In mid-September, I started noticing a tingling sensation in my fingertips and the soles of my feet. This marked the onset of peripheral neuropathy, a side effect of my chemotherapy treatment. Initially, it felt like a minor annoyance, but as the weeks went by, the discomfort intensified.

Over the next few months, the tingling evolved into a more significant issue. The soles of my feet became completely numb. My toes began to feel as if they were wrapped in cobwebs, a sensation that was both strange and unsettling.

This peripheral neuropathy became the most notable side effect of my chemotherapy journey. While I had anticipated some side effects, this symptom took me by surprise. It served as a constant reminder of the treatment's toll on my body, impacting my daily life in ways I hadn't expected.

OCTOBER EXHAUSTION

After a busy September, I found myself completely wiped out in October. Looking back, the month feels like a blur. I remember feeling more exhausted than ever before, dealing with persistent bone spurs, mouth pain and worsening peripheral neuropathy. It was the toughest month I faced since starting chemotherapy.

I ended up pulling six bone spurs out of my lower left gum that grew out of my jaw. The first one started in mid-July and they just kept forming. One would come out and another would grow. The last one I had removed by my dentist. This was not a normal side effect. No one at BC Cancer or my dentist had heard of this happening from chemo. But, I have no other explanation.

Bone Spur Removal *I pulled six of these suckers out—painful, annoying, and relentless. This one was the biggest.*

What struck me as odd was that even though I had completed my chemotherapy six weeks prior, the side effects seemed to hit me harder than ever. The doctors had warned me that the effects of chemotherapy would be cumulative, and it became clear to me just how true that was.

All I could manage during this time was to rest. My fitness and exercise goals were put on hold; I struggled just to get out of bed, move to the couch, and then back to bed. This was the period when chemotherapy's impact was fully felt, and I realized I was truly in the thick of it.

Ultimately, I had to listen to my body, accepting that rest was my priority. It was a challenging time, but I understood that this phase was part of the healing process.

NOVEMBER 1 – Mental Struggles and Diet Setbacks

The past month has been relentless. I've felt unwell every

single day—exhausted to the core, physically and mentally drained. Most nights, I was out cold by 8:00 or 8:30 PM, but rarely did I sleep through the night. I'd wake up groggy, use the bathroom, and often crash again until 11, noon, or even later.

That was the routine. Day after day, for nearly ten weeks post-chemo. Aside from a few short outings with family or 2–3 km walks with D'Arcy and Danny, I was on the couch or in bed. If I wasn't horizontal inside, I was lying in the hammock outside until the weather turned.

What's strange is that I had more energy in September than I did in October—when I thought I'd be steadily regaining strength. Instead, it felt like I was going backward. It was disheartening. I expected some fatigue, but I didn't expect this slow, grinding depletion.

That's something people don't talk about enough: just how long recovery from chemo takes. The fatigue doesn't pass in a few days or even weeks. It lingers, weighs on every movement, fogs up your mind. Healing is slow, inconsistent, and often invisible.

My neuropathy worsened during this period—tingling and numbness began in my toes and fingertips and spread to my soles and heels. Stretching intensified the pins and needles, especially when reaching down to touch my toes or extending my arms backward. Playing guitar, bass, or piano became impossible. I really hope this fades with time.

My mental state followed my physical one—slipping into negativity, fog, and frustration. After Danny left at the end of September, I stopped exercising altogether. My diet fell apart. I was stress-eating—plant-based ice cream, sugary bubble tea, cookies, brownies, chips. Less vegetables and lean meats. More burgers, meat pies, and steaks. I gained 20 pounds back in just two months.

I also slipped back into drinking—4 to 6 drinks, 3 to 5 nights a week. I'd smoke a pre-rolled hybrid joint or use cannabis tinctures to unwind. At first, it felt like a release. I bought three more joints, but after smoking two, I started noticing the connection between my low energy, dark moods, and the weed. Two weeks ago, I tossed the last one.

These weren't just minor setbacks. They were red flags—reminders that the healing process isn't just about finishing treatment. It's about rebuilding every system, every habit, from the ground up. And sometimes, it takes slipping to remember how much I want to rise.

Managing Neuropathy and Moving Forward

I started pushing myself to exercise more toward the end of October, managing to go for several walks or hikes. I experienced significant muscle pain in my glutes, hamstrings, and left Achilles tendon and heel. For the pins and needles, I stretched my hands, fingers, toes, legs, & calves and used a foot bath and roller throughout the day. While that helped somewhat, the overall numbness persists without full resolution.

The neuropathy is strongest on the bottoms of my feet. My hands are most affected at the fingertips, but the effect has also spread around my palms and wrists.

Facing Mortality

The lead-up to surgery was difficult. I struggled with the harsh reality that every living thing will eventually die. Is cancer going to take me out? I fought so hard. I love D'Arcy immensely; I have never experienced the true unconditional love that she shows me. I love my parents and kids so much.

> *"Sun is the same, in a relative way, but you're older*
> *Shorter of breath and one day closer to death."*
> *— Pink Floyd, "Time"*

My children—Aidan, Linda, Niall, and Lauren—are fantastic: loving, affectionate, funny, and incredibly smart. They're also responsible individuals who've been living independently for many years. Watching them grow into their adult lives brings me endless joy. We all get along effortlessly and make each other laugh constantly—there's a special kind of rhythm in our connection. And then there's my grandkids, Oliver and Noah. Watching them come into their own—curious, kind, and full of life—fills me with pride and excitement. I can't wait to see the people they become. I have so much to live for. I haven't pulled through this yet, but I carry the willpower, strength, and purpose to do it.

Surgery Preparations and Fear of a Stoma

I received a call from VGH, informing me that I might need a stoma. A stoma is a surgically created opening in the abdomen that allows waste to exit the body when the lower digestive tract can't function normally. In my case, it would involve bringing a portion of the colon—or in some cases, the rectum—through the abdominal wall, where waste would then be collected in an external bag attached to the skin. Depending on the outcome of surgery and the location and extent of tissue removed, a stoma can be either temporary or permanent. The idea of waking up with one terrified me. Alongside that fear was another: the massive incision I knew would stretch from my sternum to my pelvis. And deeper still, the unspoken dread that something might go wrong during surgery and I could die on the table. As these thoughts circled through my mind in the two weeks leading up to surgery, I made another firm commitment to myself—I quit consuming alcohol and cannabis again. I wanted to face this moment with total clarity and strength.

Bob Cain is at **Jug Island, Belcarra.**
Nov 5 ·

Phase 3 - HIPEC Surgery

In less than 48 hours my life will be in the hands of the fine surgeons at Vancouver General Hospital. Their mission - remove any and all cancer in my colon and abdomen while bringing me back safe and sound, cancer free.... See more

Lauren Cain and 133 others   100 comments

***Quiet Before the Storm** I perched myself at the end of a tree branch, taking a moment for stillness and reflection the day before surgery.*

CHAPTER 7

CYTOREDUCTIVE/HIPEC SURGERY

"I've seen fire and I've seen rain / I've seen sunny days that I thought would never end."
— James Taylor, "Fire and Rain" (1970)

Nov 7 – Into the Fire

The day began at 3:45 AM with bowel prep. I took a long, hot shower and let the water pour over me while I meditated. I was calm. Focused. I knew what was coming. I got dressed, and we drove through the dark, silent streets to the hospital. It was 5:15 AM. I felt ready—or as ready as you can be before a massive, life-altering surgery.

After checking in and moving through pre-op, I met Melanie, the nurse in the recovery area who would be looking after me post-surgery. I changed into a gown and began speaking with the surgical team—residents, anesthesiologists, and doctors—each one walking me through their role and what was about to happen.

Dr. MacNeill and Dr. Vasulyeva would be leading the HIPEC surgery together. They explained they'd be operating in tandem, taking turns and spelling each other off depending on how long the procedure lasted. Dr. MacNeill reassured me that the combination of my CT scan and the recent laparoscopy looked promising. The cancer hadn't spread beyond what they had already planned to remove.

She called it a "pretty standard case," expected to take 8 to 9 hours. That was exactly what I needed to hear right before being wheeled into the operating room. A standard procedure. Breathe, Bob. This will all be over in the blink of an eye.

Then came the OR—bright lights, machines, a dozen professionals, and the sound of preparation all around me. I was helped onto the table and sat upright while they inserted three epidural needles into my back to numb the abdomen. Then I lay back down. A mask went over my face.

"We're putting you to sleep now."

Everything went black.

When I came to, I was back in recovery. My entire body was shaking. I was freezing cold. And my shoulders and arms were on fire. Apparently, I'd been strapped down with both arms splayed outward for the duration of the surgery—14 hours.

It wasn't supposed to take that long.

I could barely move. My throat was raw from the breathing tube. I had IVs in both arms and my neck. A catheter. An oxygen line. A drainage tube through my nose into my belly. I was wired up like a cyborg.

I stayed in that bed all night with a nurse sitting beside me, monitoring every vital sign. My heart rate. My oxygen levels. My blood pressure. I drifted in and out of consciousness, still not quite believing I'd made it through.

But I had.

I was still here.

Nov 8–13 – Step-Down Unit

At 8 AM the next morning, a transporter wheeled me to the 8th-floor step-down unit. The hallway lights blurred past me, and I remember thinking: *So begins the next chapter*. Once in my new room—four beds, four curtains, and two nurses per patient—a soft voice greeted me.

"Hello, Mr. Cain. My name is Mia, and I'll be your nurse today. May I take your temperature and blood pressure?"

That simple act—her gentle touch on my arm, the steadiness in her voice—grounded me.

The days that followed passed in a strange, dreamlike blur. The nights were long and chaotic. I soaked my sheets four or five times a night with fever sweats. My body swung between bone-deep chills and scorching heat, the blankets alternately too much and never enough.

The hydromorphone helped with the pain but blurred the line between sleep and delirium. Every time I closed my eyes, vivid hallucinations played like short films on repeat—abstract, unsettling, sometimes terrifying. I'd wake unsure of where I was or what was real.

Social Wave – Nov 8, 2024

After a 14 hour surgery, I'm happy to report I'm cancer free. Now for the trip down recovery road to full health. I'm happy to be alive!

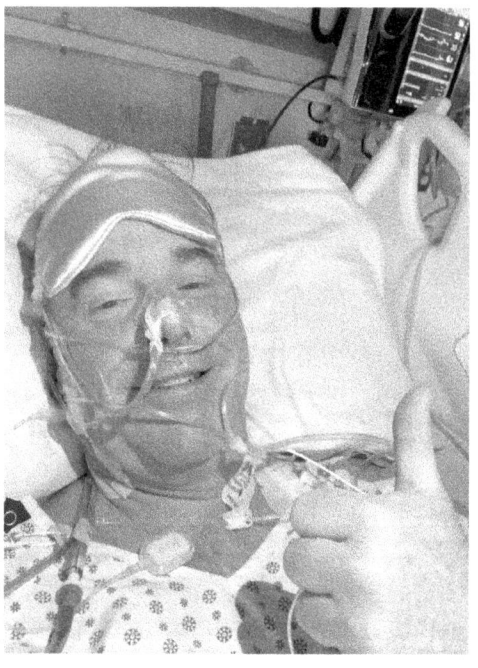

   335   189

I remember the nurses best: Ellie, Mia, Sakshi, Zene, Jen, Brenda. They changed shifts every 12 hours—7 to 7—but no matter the time, they were always there. Quick, compassionate, efficient. Angels in scrubs.

Through it all, I focused on one thing: survival. One moment at a time. One breath, one sip of water, one whispered check-in from a nurse. I couldn't do much else. That was the work—just being there. Letting my body recover while my mind slowly found its way back.

Hallucinations

On the fourth night, I began experiencing severe night sweats followed by intermittent periods of intense shivering cold. When I closed my eyes, I started having vivid hallucinations — so real that I couldn't tell whether I was dreaming or awake.

With my eyes open, I could see the four curtain walls around me. I knew I was in the step-down recovery room on the ninth floor at Vancouver General Hospital. But the moment I closed my eyes, the world transformed.

Colours appeared like shifting fish scales — intensely vivid reds, greens, and blues. Scenes unfolded that I can only describe as deeply otherworldly. I saw many of my friends, but their faces were distorted — ogre-like, with sharp, pointed ears and oversized eyes. Faces emerged from cavern walls as though I were walking through long underground passages. At the same time, I could still hear the sounds of the other patients in the room. I would open my eyes, and there were the four curtains again.

It was the strangest hallucination I've ever experienced — and I say that having experimented with LSD in my youth.

At the time, I was on 10 mg of oral hydromorphone — the maximum dose for someone my size — in addition to four epidural lines in my back delivering more hydromorphone to control post-operative pain. It was simply too much for my system.

Thank goodness Ellie was there.

She stayed calm, grounded, and present, helping me regulate my temperature — cooling me when I was overheating, wrapping me in warm blankets when the chills took over. She talked with me, anchored me, and helped me through the night.

The following day, the team began stepping down my pain medication. By night seven, the hallucinations had stopped completely, and my pain was manageable with T3s.

Ellie is an angel among us.

D'Arcy and I became friends with her over those nights. She's also a singer, and we bonded over music, even talking about jamming together once I was out of the hospital. I told her I was writing a book about my cancer journey called *24HrDay* and that I'd love to give her a copy when it was finished.

She gave us her email so we could stay in touch.

Thank you, Ellie.

Bernie

The other nurse who helped carry me through those long day shifts was **Bernie**. Like Ellie, she's highly experienced and has worked on this unit for a long time.

The two of them worked seamlessly together — almost like a relay team — making sure I was as comfortable as possible over a full 24-hour cycle. When you're living inside a hospital routine like that, having nurses who communicate well and genuinely care makes an enormous difference.

I'm deeply grateful to both of them. They told me they're excited to read this book once it's published, and I promised I'd bring copies back for the unit when it's done. I absolutely will.

Nov 11: Remembrance and Reflection

Remembrance Day and Niall's birthday. I've been on hydromorphone—2 mg every three hours for the past three days and nights. On top of that, my epidural was maxed out at level 10. They couldn't give me anymore.

By the fourth night, I added Zopiclone to help me sleep. Still, the rest was fragmented and shallow. Tylenol and Benadryl came every six hours to manage the fever and the relentless itching that had become my constant companion. Ice packs were my only real relief—nurses brought them without asking, draping them across my arms like armor against the fire under my skin.

The discomfort was relentless. My upper lip was badly swollen from the breathing tube. My throat was raw, stinging like strep. The pain settled mostly in my chest and belly, but the itching—God, the itching—was the worst of it. By day three, the fever sweats started like clockwork: 2 PM for two hours, then again after midnight. My fever stayed under 38.5°C, but my body was at war.

At 1:41 AM, I hadn't slept a wink despite the meds. My mind wandered to darker places. Since Trump's re-election on November 4th, I'd quit reading the news. It was all too much. The division. The noise. The illusion of information without wisdom. I started to wonder whether any of it helped anyone. Most people seem deeply unhappy, locked into angry opinions, forgetting how to simply connect.

These days, I don't debate. I listen. I let people vent, if they need to, and offer a little kindness. I've stopped feeding the outrage machine. Maybe that's the only way to stay sane.

Despite the chaos of the last few days, I had one enormous blessing: D'Arcy. She stayed with me every day, every night—present, grounded, unwavering. I love her so much. She is perfect for me.

By mid-afternoon, when the physiotherapist hadn't shown,

D'Arcy and I tried walking the halls on our own. We did 400 steps. No walker, no nurse. Just me, slowly putting one foot in front of the other. I later sat upright in a chair for 35 minutes and used the foot massager to ease the numbness in my toes. It felt incredible to give my feet that attention.

My arms and legs were covered in little scabs from all the scratching, but D'Arcy gently rubbed moisturizer into my skin. That moment—her hands, the silence, the care—was the most healing part of the entire day.

Nov 13: The Return of the Fart

The days and nights are passing by, and I find myself feeling almost unfazed by everything at this point. Over the last 72 hours, I've been experiencing cold sweats that begin roughly 10 minutes after each hydromorphone injection. These episodes can last anywhere from one to two hours. Sometimes I wake up feeling cold and wet, while other times, I'm fully awake during the entire episode. After about one to two hours, my face, head, and hair are completely soaked. I often have cold packs under my arms and at the back of my neck to help manage the discomfort. My arms, legs, and torso feel moist and cold, and my pillowcases, gown, and sheets typically end up wet as well. We usually change the bed sheets and my gown three to four times a day.

Additionally, I've been dealing with a dry mouth, swollen lips, and a constantly sore throat. Occasionally, these "hot flashes," as the nurses call them, are accompanied by headaches.

During the daylight and early evening hours, I pass the time lying on my back under the sheets, watching shows on Apple+ or catching DAZN games on my computer. This distraction provides a nice break from the discomfort. I keep myself occupied by chewing gum and sucking on throat lozenges to ease my dry mouth.

My dressings had to be changed multiple times a day thanks to all the sweating, but miraculously, my temperature held steady between 36°C and 38.5°C. Still, I was on day six without food or drink, and my body was starting to feel it. Time moved strangely slow, foggy, but forward. Each hour held its own blend of discomfort, restlessness, and fleeting distraction.

The ability to lie still and breathe deeply became one of my greatest assets. All those years of practicing transcendental meditation had finally paid off. It was one of the few things I could actually do—and it helped.

Then, at exactly 10:07 AM on November 12, it happened: I let out a slow, steady, three-second fart. The first gas in almost a week. It was glorious. I felt a little buzz of joy shoot through me. Something had finally moved.

Moments later, I felt another one coming. I gave a gentle push—and promptly shat the bed. It was messy and, at first, humiliating. But the nurses were not phased. Poops and farts are celebrated on this floor. "This is a good sign," one of them said. "Your system is waking up." And she was right. My gut had officially rejoined the recovery process. In a strange way, I felt proud.

Over the next two days, I had several more bowel movements—some in a diaper, some successfully on the toilet—and none of it was as bad as I had feared. These awkward, raw and real moments became milestones. I was moving forward, inch by inch, breath by breath. Shit by messy shit.

The night of the 12th brought my best sleep all week: a full stretch from 10 PM to 6:30 AM. The next morning, I began tapering off Tylenol and spaced out the hydromorphone from every three hours to every five or six. My body was adapting.

Then came the big steps: they removed the abdominal drain and the NG tube into my stomach that had been running through my nose—which had been contributing to the raw soreness in my throat. A few hours later, it was time to remove the chest drain.

During surgery, chest and abdominal drains were placed to help remove fluid and promote healing. The chest drain connected to an underwater-seal system evacuated air or fluid from the lung area. The abdominal drain funnelled fluid into a collection bag at my incision site. Both systems worked continuously, helping my body clear excess fluid and reduce the risk of complications while I recovered

The chest drain line was massive—about three feet long and a quarter inch thick, used to draw blood and serum from the peritoneum. The doctor gave it a single, decisive pull that lasted three to five seconds. It wasn't exactly painful, but it was…uncomfortable. There's always a risk of the lung shifting or collapsing during this procedure, but I was lucky. My chest X-ray came back clean.

Buoyed by that win, I managed to walk a few laps around the ward solo with my IV stand. That day I peed three times and had two more bowel movements. Liquid, dark brown—evidence that my digestive system was getting back online.

Every little victory mattered. And today was full of them.

Nov 14 – *View from the Other Side*

Later that day, I was moved out of the step-down recovery unit into a semi-private room. It was a welcome change—quieter, brighter, and with a nice view out the window. I could feel the shift, both physically and mentally. I was making progress.

Still, the relentless sweating continued—on and off for four straight days. I wasn't sure if it was the hydromorphone or something else, but the discomfort pushed me to make a change. I decided to stop the hydromorphone and switch to T3s. Within 24 hours, the sweats began to ease. But then came the constipation. Always a trade-off. It's clear that I'll need to start weaning off the pain meds altogether if I want my digestive system to reset.

Despite all this, I feel encouraged. The worst seems behind me, and my body is starting to rebound. Every day I move a little more. Eat a little more. Sleep a little better.

Looking back on the week—and really, the last year—I'm struck by the sheer scale of it all. The fear, the suffering, the brief reprieves, the exhausting cycles of pain and hope. When I string it all together, what I see isn't just a fight against cancer. It's a chance. A real, tangible chance to extend my life and transform it. To heal what can be healed. To live better, deeper, clearer.

I know death is not done with me—it never is. It will return, someday, and there may come a time when I don't have the strength to fight it off. And that, too, will be okay. When the day comes, I will have faced it knowing I lived with courage, intention, and as much grace as I could summon.

But that day is not today. Today, I live. Today, I prepare myself to live fully—with clarity, discipline, and purpose. There's a new kind of power in that decision. A quiet resolve. And it carries me forward.

Nov 15: Going Home

Today is the day I go home from the hospital—and it's a beautiful, sunny day.

Last night marked my sixth straight night of discomfort. The sweats came twice, soaking through my gown and sheets. I had to call for fresh linens just to stay warm enough to sleep. But even so, I woke up with a sense of anticipation. I'm ready.

This morning, I met with an occupational therapist who helped us gather the essentials—grab bars, seat risers, a few key supports to make sure I can move safely around the bathroom once I'm home. One of the nurses came in to remove the last abdominal drain and apply a fresh dressing that will stay on for the next five days. With every piece of tubing gone, I feel lighter. Less tethered. More human again.

The past week has been the hardest of my life. Fever dreams. Hallucinations. Night sweats. Shivering under cold, wet sheets. Pain that came in waves and disorientation that blurred the edges of reality. But somehow, amidst it all, there were moments of joy. The first time I could stand. The first independent walk. Sitting up. Drinking. Eating. Passing gas. Peeing. Pooping. It all sounds so basic, but each one was a small triumph—proof that my body was coming back online. I swear I heard angels sing.

Through all of it, D'Arcy has been extraordinary. By my side every day for 8 to 10 hours—steady, loving, intuitive. She anticipated what I needed before I could say it out loud. She's been my anchor. My rock star. I truly don't know how I could've gotten through this without her.

As I prepare to leave the hospital, I'm filled with gratitude and a quiet kind of joy. The thought of the drive home, the crisp air on my face, and returning to our cozy little place in Coquitlam feels almost surreal. My mom arrives tomorrow, and she will be a huge support.

Once I'm home, I plan to ease into my routine again—short walks, gentle stretches, breath-work, meditation. I'm still in pain, and I know the road ahead is long, but I also know this: I've turned a corner. I've survived the fire. Now it's time to rebuild, day by day.

A mural downtown Vancouver that kind says it all.

Nov 18: Day Four at Home

This is my fourth day at home, and it's been hard. The night sweats continue—three or four times each night—leaving me soaked and chilled, my sheets needing to be changed just to stay warm.

The first two days were especially rough. I was badly constipated and bloated, unable to eat, and increasingly uncomfortable. I made the call to stop the T3s. They always dehydrate me and lock everything up, and right now, the only way to heal is to eat. I'm choosing manageable pain over malnourishment. By day three, there were signs of movement—wet spurts and gas. Not glamorous, but it meant my system was waking up. The pain in my arms and abdomen is slightly worse with just Tylenol, but compared to the discomfort of constipation, it's a trade-off I'm willing to make.

Every evening at 6 PM, I give myself a blood thinner injection to prevent clots. It's a bit of a ritual now: prep the syringe, pick the spot, breathe deeply, and press it in. It's not fun, but it matters—and that makes it easier to face.

Today, day four, I managed two walks with my mom—about 700 steps total. It felt good to get outside, even though the cold hit me harder than usual. I also showered for the first time since surgery. At 11 days post-op, a shower and two walks feel like real progress.

Mom's been amazing, always there with food, warmth, care and conversation. And D'Arcy… I don't even have words. She gets up 8 or 9 times a night to help me—changing sheets, soothing me, making sure I'm comfortable. Her love and devotion have been nothing short of heroic. I owe her my deepest gratitude. She's been everything.

I honestly don't know how anyone does this alone. I couldn't. Without D'Arcy and my mom, this would be unimaginable. Their presence is my safety net, and I'm clinging to it with everything I've got.

CHAPTER 8

RECOVERY ROAD

"And at once I knew I was not magnificent…"
— *Bon Iver, "Holocene" (2011)*

HOME AGAIN, BUT NOT THE SAME

This is the hardest part of the journey so far. I'm a shell of my regular self—so weak, in pain, hunched over, and walking like an 80-year-old man. I can't care for myself without help, can't get comfortable, and it's very hard to sleep. The moment I fall asleep I'm awakened by the cold soaking wet feeling of night sweats.

One step at a time, one day at a time. I will heal, and this will pass. Time moves slowly, but it does pass. I must take each passing day as a win. I'm alive after all, and I have my life in front of me. I just have to press through. Tomorrow is another day, one step closer to feeling healthy again.

Neuropathy Sets In

The neuropathy in my hands and feet has worsened. I can now feel it in my face too, primarily on the bridge of my nose and my cheeks, with the left cheek being more affected. I would grade that pain at 2/10. My hands feel like 6/10 in severity, while my feet are at 8/10. I've also noticed a slight sensation in my calves when I bend over or stretch my legs out. My toes feel extremely tight, and my fingertips are super sensitive—almost painful when I put pressure on them. The discomfort intensifies when I stretch or bend my arms back.

NOVEMBER 19: Out for a Drive

I'm still sweating badly throughout the night. I got up to move to the couch to help D'Arcy get some sleep. I grabbed a popsicle and decided to take the car out for a drive—a short escape to somewhere peaceful, like Lake Sasamat. Tesla's free month of self-driving made the trip even easier.

Nov 20 – Forty-Seven Staples

Today was rough.

I had all 47 staples removed from my surgical site by my family doctor, Dr. Rashid and nurse Amy at the Plateau Medical Clinic in Coquitlam B.C. I'd been anxious about it all morning—for good reason. The whole process took nearly an hour, with about 45 minutes spent removing staples, one by one.

Amy began by cleaning each wound and gently peeling off the sticky bandage glue. Right away, we hit a complication: the chest drain wound had opened and needed to be closely monitored. Then we discovered that the main stitched section near my belly button had also opened up, oozing pus around a few embedded staples.

It was painful. But Amy and Dr. Rashid moved swiftly, working as a team. My mom was at my feet, massaging them, while D'Arcy stood by my side, letting me crush her fingers each time they yanked out another staple. The ones near the infection felt like bee stings—sharp, shocking. Probably 20 of them were brutal. Others weren't as bad, where the skin had healed cleanly. Still, it took everything in me to stay still.

Now I'm home, lying on the couch, trying not to move. I've got two more antibiotics to finish and a follow-up with Dr. Vasulyeva in three days.

I feel fragile, like I'm made of paper and stitches—but I'm also incredibly grateful. Mom and D'Arcy were my lifelines in that room. Their calm and care helped carry me through. I don't know what I would've done without them.

Oh—and because nothing comes easy, I found out I've got a mild case of athlete's foot to deal with, too. One thing at a time. Just keep healing.

November 23: Sleepless Nights

As usual, I find myself unable to sleep. My abdomen feels tight, and I'm lying primarily on my back, trying to remain as still as possible to allow my wounds to heal. My mind is restless, replaying the events of the last 12 months repeatedly.

Today marked a significant milestone: it was the first day I had to clean my wounds and change my dressings. Unfortunately, the main suture has opened up, extending from just above my belly button to about three inches below it. It's 3–4 cm, with the skin pulling apart and showing signs of infection. The chest wound is also gaping and needs close monitoring.

I know I need to take it easy over the next few weeks and hope that these wounds will begin to close properly. I continue to treat the neuropathy with foot baths, massage, stretching, walking, and a TENS machine. These methods have become essential tools in my recovery process.

Even though the nights are long and filled with discomfort, I remain focused on my healing journey. I'm committed to taking care of myself by taking the necessary steps to recover fully.

NOVEMBER 27: Wound Setbacks

It's been five days since the staples were removed, and the wound immediately opened up around my belly button, as well as a few inches above and below. It is now a gaping wound measuring 4–5 cm that constantly oozes pus like substance known as slough.

Much of my time has been spent on the couch or in bed, trying to manage my pain. I'm currently on several medications, including blood thinners. Every night at 7:00 PM, I perform a daily injection in alternating thighs. I can't help but wonder if the blood thinners have contributed to the improper healing of my incision.

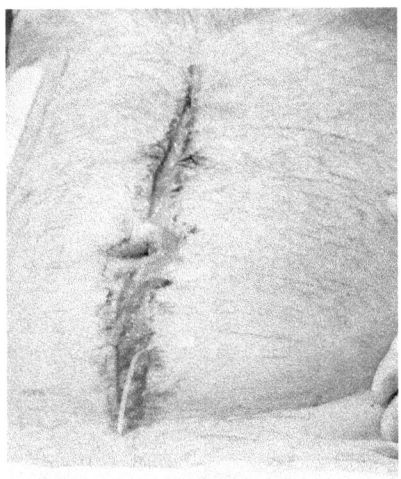

Post-Surgery Setback *The entire 27 cm incision reopened after the staples were removed—a tough setback. I've since learned this is not uncommon for patients who haven't fully recovered from chemotherapy before surgery.*

Despite the difficulties, Mom and D'Arcy have been incredibly supportive. However, all three of us have had moments of frustration. Today I'm seeing a wound care nurse for the first time. These appointments will occur every other day until my wound is fully healed.

I've walked about 0.75 km around Lafarge Lake with Mom and D'Arcy, though the wound setback has been discouraging. Still, I drew strength from the Terry Fox Training Route.

Today's wound assessment: 21 cm long, 3 cm wide, and 0.5cm deep. Severity rated 3/10.

I just wanted this part to be over.

November 28: Progress and Reflection

It's been three full weeks since surgery, and today was my best day yet for energy.

This morning, Mom and I walked 2.5 km around Buntzen Lake—the most strenuous walk I've done so far. Later in the evening, we added another kilometre around Como Lake with our headlamps lighting the way. It felt good. My goal is to gradually build up to 5 km a day.

Everyday tasks are getting easier, too. I can now dress myself, put on and tie my shoes, and I've even started driving again. Small victories, but they matter.

That said, the neuropathy remains a concern. It's still as intense as ever—no signs of improvement. Sleep is another ongoing challenge. Even though I'm in bed for 12 hours most nights, my watch tells me I'm only averaging about 7.5 hours of actual sleep. Constant waking continues to disrupt my rest.

Still, I feel progress. And for now, that's enough to keep me going.

December 2: *Gratitude and Progress*

As my mom prepared to fly back to Ontario, I was overwhelmed with gratitude for the love, care, and steady presence she offered throughout my recovery—and my life. She's been more than a supportive mother. She's been a quiet force of inspiration.

The older I get, the more I've come to admire her grace in the face of adversity. She's navigated periods of immense pain and challenge with strength, humility, and intelligence. I'm so fortunate to have a mom who, at 82, is still as vibrant, witty, and full of life as she was at 42. And anyone who knows her would say the same—she's truly amazing.

I've noticed an increase in my mobility, allowing me to engage in light activities and stretching without as much hesitation. They also serve as a pleasant way to ease boredom, providing a little enjoyment during recovery.

Wound Care – *Nov 25 to Dec 23*

The care I received at the wound care clinic in Port Moody, B.C. was consistently excellent. The nurses were gentle, friendly, and highly skilled trained to be precise and quick without compromising comfort.

I discovered that the best way to get through each session was to lie flat on my back, close my eyes, and focus on slow, steady breathing. Meditating through the treatment helped when I stayed present with my breath, I barely felt a thing. Strangely, watching the procedure made it feel more painful. I've always had sensitivity around my belly button, so learning to manage this discomfort felt like a small victory.

The treatments spanned from November 25 to December 23—a total of 12 sessions. For the final six, they used a vacuum-seal dressing, which significantly accelerated healing. The results were remarkable. Over the last two weeks, I could visibly see my wound improving. That visible progress lifted my spirits and renewed my sense of optimism.

Social Wave – Dec 12, 2024

It's been five weeks since surgery. 47 staples were removed from the incision three weeks ago. 14 days following surgery is the standard time for staple removal. During the procedure, a few spots opened up. Within four days the entire wound opened up superficially. Since then, I've been going to a wound care clinic twice a week and will continue for 2-3 more weeks. Had my sixth appointment at the clinic yesterday. I'm happy to report the wound is healing and the skin is now growing back. I'm grateful for the health care we get in Canada. There has been help and support at every turn and the care has been great.

It's rare that wounds will open after staples are removed. Turns out my body has still not recovered from the chemo. My hemoglobin is still only at 65% of where it was when I started chemo. So that's the reason for the set back. Should make for a fun looking scar, no? Sort of looks like Voldemort got me good.

This cancer fighting business is a long, gruelling process. I'm grateful to be in the winning side of the battle. Thank you from the bottom of my heart for all the messages, well wishes and prayers. I felt them all, they carried me though to this point.

   132   33

A Quiet Christmas

By the time Christmas arrived, I was finally beginning to feel like myself again. I had completed my wound care just a few days earlier, and my energy was noticeably better. I could move around more easily, and the fog of pain and fatigue had begun to lift.

D'Arcy and I chose to stay home and keep things simple—a quiet Christmas, just the two of us—which felt exactly right. For the first time in months, it felt like we'd made it through the worst. We had turned a corner.

One of the highlights was our Christmas evening walk. We bundled up and headed to Lafarge Lake, where the holiday lights were glowing in full brilliance. We managed a peaceful 3-kilometre stroll through the displays, surrounded by the soft hum of other families doing the same.

The lights were beautiful, but more than that, the walk itself felt like a quiet celebration of everything we'd endured—of survival, resilience, and the love that carried us through. I cherished every moment with D'Arcy that night. This Christmas didn't look like any I'd had before, but in many ways, it meant more. It marked a turning point—a moment to recognize how far I'd come, and how deeply grateful I was for the love, support, and presence surrounding me.

Bob and D'Arcy at Lafarge Lake - Christmas Eve.

Celebrating New Year's

A few days after Christmas, D'Arcy and I felt ready to reconnect with friends, and there was no better way to do that than spending New Year's Eve with Alex and Raji. They had been pillars of support throughout my journey, and it meant the world to finally share an evening with them that felt celebratory rather than solemn.

Social Wave – Jan 31, 2024

Happy New Year! Let's go 2025.

   140   41

Alex, a restaurant consultant and an absolutely brilliant chef, cooked what might have been the best steak dinner of my life—rich, perfectly seasoned, and somehow symbolic of being alive to taste life fully again.

As the clock struck midnight, we raised our glasses and toasted to new beginnings, to resilience, and to the hope of a healthier, brighter year ahead. It felt like a true celebration—not just of the New Year, but of everything we had endured and overcome. That night was more than a party. It was a deep exhale after a long, painful stretch of holding my breath.

As January unfolded, I could feel my body getting stronger with each passing day. The exhaustion and uncertainty that had gripped me for so long began to fade. For the first time, I felt like I was truly on the other side of the battle.

January – Reclaiming Life

When Lauren arrived in early January, we spent a few beautiful days exploring Vancouver before heading to Revelstoke to visit Aidan, Linda, and the kids. This wasn't just a family trip—it was a celebration. A celebration of life, of healing, and of being cancer-free.

At Aidan's, we relaxed into the rhythm of family—playing games, sharing meals, going for walks, even skiing one day. There was laughter, warmth, and a quiet sense of awe from everyone seeing me back on my feet after such a long, brutal road. Their support was steady and heartfelt, and it touched me deeply to be surrounded by people who had held space for my struggle and now stood beside me in recovery.

These days together weren't just fun; they were sacred. They reminded me how far I'd come and what mattered most. Each hug, each shared meal, each glide down the slopes was a kind of miracle—a living reminder of why I fought so hard.

Throughout the rest of January, I pushed myself physically, gradually building up my strength. By the end of the month, I was closing in on the health stats I had back in April, just before I began chemotherapy. When I tallied everything, the numbers confirmed it: I had essentially returned to baseline. After a surgery that typically requires 3 to 6 months of recovery, I had reached full function in just over two. That progress was no accident.

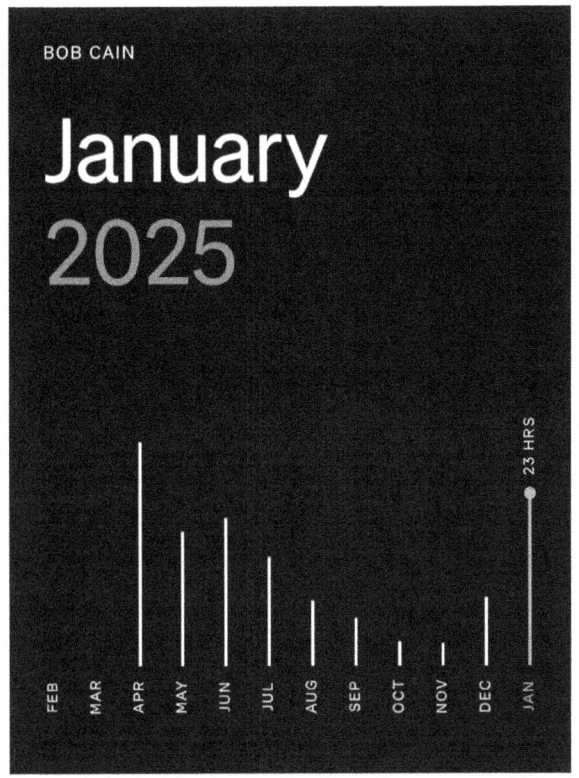

Back on Track *Solid evidence from my health tracking showed I was turning a corner after January—momentum was building again.*

Back on the Bike

A few weeks later, I took the next big step in my recovery: I got back on my mountain bike.

Mountain biking has been part of my life for 25 years—and it's one of the main reasons I moved to British Columbia. There's nothing quite like it: the physical challenge, the rush of navigating roots and rocks, the meditative rhythm of the climb, and the payoff of shredding through trails under the canopy of a B.C. rainforest. It's more than exercise—it's joy, presence, and connection all at once.

For the past year, though, biking was off-limits. My immune system was compromised by chemo, and my body just didn't have the strength and didn't want to risk injury. Every trail I passed up felt like a small loss. But I knew I'd be back—someday.

And that day finally came.

Getting back on the bike filled me with pure anticipation. It wasn't just about fitness or freedom—it was about reclaiming a piece of myself. As I peddled through the forest, I felt alive in a way I hadn't for months. The smells, the sweat, the grind of gears and rubber over dirt—all of it reminded me that healing isn't just about surviving. It's about returning to what you love.

This ride marked a turning point. I wasn't just recovering anymore. I was living again.

Social Wave – Feb 21, 2024

Back in the saddle after a year and a half hiatus from mountain biking. A couple spills. Back end slipped out once and went over the handlebars once. Yes that's mud on my face. I bounced back up no problem, feeling good as new. So nice out there crushing trails.

My first follow up CT Scan after the Nov. surgery is in an hour. I'm feeling better than I could have hoped. Results in 7-10 days. I'll be getting a CT Scan every six months the rest of my life. It's a great thing the Canadian medical system provides this free of charge for Canadian, Cancer survivors. Hopefully, this the first of the 100+ I will get in my life.

   152   23

Social Wave – Mar 5, 2024

Results are in from my post surgery CT Scan. Oncologist says there's no sign of any tumours or metastasis. Six months until my next scan. For now, I'm good to go. I'm making the most of my time. Getting strong now.

   302   126

CT Scan Results

About a week later, I went in for my first post-operative CT scan. I was both nervous and hopeful—eager to know how my body was healing after everything it had been through.

The results came back clean. Everything looked good.

Relief washed over me. It was a milestone moment—clear confirmation that my recovery wasn't just something I felt, but something my body was showing in real, measurable ways. After months of pain, fatigue, and uncertainty, this news brought renewed confidence.

More than anything, it reinforced the value of everything I'd been doing—walking, hiking, skiing, stretching, meditating, tracking my habits. My body had responded. My strength and vitality were coming back.

This scan didn't just tell me I was healing—it told me I was winning.

April Rolled Around

By the time April rolled around, I was feeling phenomenal.

I had locked into a powerful routine, and my *24HrDay* plan was working beautifully. My habits were fully dialled in and aligned with the life I had always dreamed of. I was hard at work on finishing the *24HrDay* book and was on track to hit my June deadline. My fitness levels were beginning to exceed my pre-cancer baseline, and my mindset was sharper, more determined, and more focused than ever before. I genuinely believed I was transforming into the very best version of myself.

This is when I began using a more advanced version of the *24HrDay* Tracker I'd built in Excel. It had grown into a seven-page spreadsheet that collected data on every measurable aspect of my life. I tracked anything I believed—if done consistently—would help me live my best life, day by day, week by week, month by month.

April also brought my birthday, and it was an awesome one. D'Arcy and four of my closest longtime friends—Lindsay, Heather, Alex, and Raji—got together for a roller-skating night in Vancouver. Total '80s throwback. I only wiped out once—right into the bumper of a food truck. Ouch. But I bounced right back up. One solid bruise. Totally worth it.

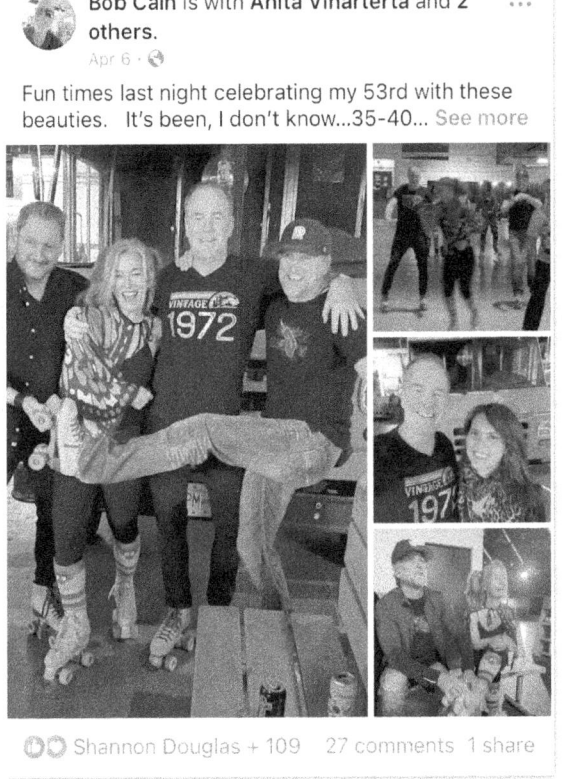

Bob's 53rd birthday with D'Arcy and lifelong friends - Lindsay, Heather, Alex and Raji

The best part? I truly felt fully recovered and cancer-free. I had done it. I had beaten cancer—and I was writing a book to tell the world exactly how I did it.

It was such an exciting time in my life.

CHAPTER 9

THE 24HRDAY BLUEPRINT

"Act the way you'd like to be and soon you'll be the way you act."
— Leonard Cohen, *The Favourite Game*

Where the Road Led Me

Fifteen months after my diagnosis, in the spring of 2024, I had done what many thought was impossible. Not only was I recovering—I was thriving.

Spring had returned to British Columbia, and with it came a new energy. I was working out consistently and living a full, intentional life every single day, seven days a week. I had never felt stronger, or more self-assured about my future, than I did at that point in time.

I had regained 100% of the strength I'd lost during my illness. In fact, my energy levels had not only returned to pre-diagnosis levels—they had improved. I felt like I had been given a second chance at life at age 53. The neuropathy in my feet was still present, but even that had started to respond to stretching, massage, and contrast (hot/cold) therapy. Maybe, with time, it would fully heal. I learned that neuropathy could take up to two years to resolve.

I was consistently sleeping better than I had in the past 20 years—averaging 7.5 hours per night. I walked 5–7 kilometres a day. I did yoga stretches in the morning. I tracked my nutrition, my finances, my relationships, and even my home and car maintenance. I had also taken back control of my attention, limiting time spent scrolling social media, reading the news, or zoning out in front of the TV. That alone gave me back hours of presence each day.

I was maintaining over 50 daily micro-habits using a custom-built spreadsheet—one I designed for myself, but that I believe could help others too.

I created a system that made every day a win—even if I never left the house.

Progress doesn't come from willpower alone—it comes from structure, consistency, and love.

This chapter isn't just a victory lap. It's a distillation. Because I want you to understand what got me here—and how you can apply it to whatever challenge you're facing.

24HrDay Methodology

A simple system. A powerful result.

Here's how it works:

1.

Track the Day, Every Day

Use a spreadsheet, an app, or even a notebook—it

doesn't matter. What matters is that you record what you do, what you eat, how you move, and how you feel - whatever your goals may be. Every day.

2. Define What Matters Most

Start by identifying 5–10 core habits. These can be anything meaningful to you. For me, this included:

Physical fitness metrics like calories burned and steps walked

Mental health inputs like mood, effort, and stress

Nutrition markers like protein, micronutrient, and hydration counts

Relationship tracking—how often I was connecting with key people in my life, whether by text, call, or face-to-face

My time spent exercising, stretching, meditating, practicing gratitude, and making a positive social impact with strangers

3. Customize Your Own Metrics

Design a system that reflects your life. Use numeric targets (e.g., 2500 kcal, 8 glasses of water), binary entries (yes/no), or subjective scores (e.g., energy: 7/10). What matters is that it's meaningful *to you*.

4. Focus on Trends, Not Perfection

It's not about hitting every target, every day. It's about building momentum. Seeing streaks. Catching declines before they spiral. Aim for consistency over intensity.

5. Reflect Daily, Weekly, and Adjust Monthly

I spent about 5 minutes every night logging my day. That practice alone gave me a deep sense of purpose and satisfaction. I knew I was living intentionally. Weekly reviews showed me where I was thriving and where I was slipping.

Monthly adjustments kept me honest, adaptive, and aligned with my long-term goals.

6. Add Purpose

This isn't a productivity tool. It's a life compass. Regularly ask yourself:

"Does how I spend my day align with who I want to become?"

Tools I Used

Excel/Habit tracker App (Strides)
Apple Watch (cals, steps, heart rate, sleep)
Journal (reflection + gratitude)

Lessons from the Edge

My hope is that this book hasn't just informed you—it's moved you.

Maybe you saw your own fears in mine.

Maybe you saw new possibilities.

Maybe, just maybe, you're ready to start your own *24HrDay* practice.

What I've learned through this journey could fill another book (and in fact, it will), but here are a few hard-earned truths that have reshaped how I live, love, and lead my life:

The smallest habits can save your life.

Never underestimate the power of ten minutes of stillness. One short walk around the block. A quiet stretch. A spontaneous text or phone call to someone you love. These tiny acts accumulate—and they matter more than you think.

You are your own best healer.

Doctors and nurses can treat you, but healing? That happens through attention, discipline, and love. You must become a steward of your own body, mind, and spirit—tending to your goals, your dreams, your emotional life, your breath.

Pain has meaning.

I don't mean it's romantic or noble. But it is data. It shows you where to focus. What to release. What to shift. What to surrender. Every ache, every loss, every doubt—it's part of the conversation between your body and your spirit.

Joy is available—even in hell.

There were days I couldn't sit up without help. But then the sun would break through the window. Or I'd hear a voice I loved. Or taste something simple and beautiful. And for a moment, I was weightless. There is always joy to be found—if we're willing to see it.

We are not meant to do this alone.

D'Arcy. My mom. My kids. My friends. My nurses. My community. They made my healing possible. No journey is walked in solitude, even when we feel alone. Ask for help. Accept love. Let people in.

The Invitation

You don't need to be a cancer survivor to benefit from a 24Hr-Day. You could be recovering from grief, burnout, addiction, or heartbreak. Or maybe you're just trying to be better—to live more intentionally.

This system is adaptable, and it's free. I used a spreadsheet. You can use that. Or build your own. Or one day, maybe you'll use the **24HrDay app** that I hope to develop when resources allow.

Here's how to start:

---

1. Open a new spreadsheet. Create your own app using AI or just use a notebook.

2. List 10–20 habits or metrics that matter to you. (Start small.)

3. Track them daily. Tweak as needed.

4. Add a space for reflection, rating your energy, mood, and effort.

5. Celebrate your wins. Review every week.

This might sound simple—but if done with consistency and care, it's transformative. I am living proof of that. See Appendix A for more.

What Comes Next

As I write this, I'm healthy. Strong. Hopeful. But also aware that life doesn't follow our scripts.

I don't know what the future holds. As I grow older, it seems that life continually throws curveballs my way. Each challenge feels increasingly difficult to resolve and overcome. But that's okay. It's almost as if the universe is compelling each of us to grow by confronting and overcoming new obstacles.

We either learn and grow, or we stagnate. This may very well be a fundamental truth of life.

While I can't say for certain if this is some sort of universal truth or not, I am committed to living my best possible life with the time I have left. I will face each challenge—no matter how daunting—armed with love, resilience, gratitude, and fortitude.

My sincere hope is that this book has offered you a spark of something deeper—a model, a mindset, a method you can make your own. My wish is that you go forward and make the most of every moment in each and every 24-hour day.

As for me—well, a few weeks after writing this, something changed. A new symptom. A whisper in the body. And so, a new story begins.

But that story belongs to ***Virtuosity.***

For now, thank you for reading.

Live Fully. Track Wisely. Heal Deeply.

And never forget what you're capable of.

Before we part ways, I want to leave you with a parable that's deeply aligned with the 24HrDay philosophy:

The Bank of Time

If you had a bank that credited your account each morning with $86,400.00, that carried over no balance from day to day and allowed you to keep no cash in your account—and every evening cancelled whatever part of the amount you had failed to use during the day—what would you do? Draw every cent out, of course.

Well, you have such a bank, and its name is Time.

Every morning, it credits you with 86,400 seconds. Every night, it rules off, as lost, whatever of this you have failed to invest in good purpose. It carries over no balances. It allows no overdrafts. Each day it opens a new account with you. Each night it burns the records of the day.

If you fail to use the day's deposits, the loss is yours. There is no going back. There is no drawing against tomorrow. You must live in the present—on today's deposits. Invest it so as to get from it the utmost in health, happiness, and success.

— **Anonymous**

This book is my evidence that it's possible. That even in the face of death, we can create a way to live more fully.

APPENDIX A

BUILDING YOUR OWN 24HRDAY LIFE PLAN

"Do. Or do not. There is no try."
— Yoda, *The Empire Strikes Back*

Purpose and Context

Four months after undergoing Cytoreductive/HIPEC surgery, I built a personal life optimization system—a program to rebuild and elevate every dimension of my life. What you'll find here is not a one-size-fits-all formula. Instead, it's a living template. The categories, subcategories, criteria, goals, and target frequencies reflect what mattered most to me in my healing journey.

Everyone's needs, responsibilities, and rhythms are different. Your version of the 24HrDay will be unique to you. My hope is that this appendix inspires and equips you to build a framework that works for *your* life.

In the future, I hope to create a universal, customizable app that brings this methodology to life for others. For now, I use Microsoft Excel to log my daily activities, generate reports, and track trends over time. It takes just 10 minutes a day—and it's helped me transform my life.

Step One: Define Your Life Categories

Start by identifying the major areas of life you want to track and improve. Here were mine:

Physical Fitness – Strength, endurance, movement, and energy.

Mental Health – Emotional balance, awareness, and rest.

Nutrition – Healing through food and supplementation.

Personal Hygiene – Daily routines that boost self-worth and vitality.

Finance – Managing money with intention and sustainability.

Home and Auto Care – Maintaining a peaceful, functional environment.

Relationships – Staying connected to loved ones and community.

Creativity – Making space for joy, expression, and innovation.

Leisure – Purposeful rest and play.

Vacation – Rest, reconnection, and perspective-shifting.

Each category became a pillar of my recovery—and a building block of the life I'm creating now.

Step Two: Break Down Each Category Into Measurable Habits

For each category, I created subcategories, daily/weekly/annual targets, and clear metrics. These were tracked either automatically (via my fitness watch) or manually (in my spreadsheet). Here are examples of how it looked in practice:

Physical Fitness

Daily Steps – 10,000
Calories Burned – 600
Distance Walked – 5 km
Stretching/Yoga – 2x/week
Strength Training – 40 mins/week
Swimming – 200m/week
Contrast Therapy – 2x/week

SUP/Cycling/Golf/Skiing – Seasonally tracked

Mental Health

Mood, Stress, Effort, Energy – Scored 1–10 daily

Rest and Relaxation – 14 hrs/week

Sleep Duration – 7.5–8 hrs/night

Nutrition

Protein – 60g+/day

Fruits/Vegetables – 3+ servings/day

Water – 2.5L/day

Bowel Movements – Tracked daily for health status

Hygiene

Brush Teeth – 2x/day

Floss – Daily

Shave – 4x/week

Massage/Physio – 4x/year

Haircut/Teeth Whitening – 1x/month

Home & Auto

Tidy Home – 3x/week

Bathroom Clean – 1x/week

EV Charging – Daily

Car Interior Clean – 2x/week

Finance

Work Hours – 62 hrs/week

Earnings Target – $200/day

Savings Target – $1,000/month

Supplement Spending – $80/month

Relationships
D'Arcy – 4 hrs/day
Family/Friends – Tracked weekly, monthly, quarterly, and annually
Positive Social Impact – 3 people/day

Creativity
Journal – 10 mins/day
Book Writing – 12 hrs/week
Music – 3 hrs/week jamming, 8 hrs/quarter recording

Leisure
TV/Movies – 7 hrs/week
NFL Viewing – 7 hrs/week (Sept–Feb)
News & Social Media – 10 mins/day

Vacation
Day Trips – 2x/month (May–Oct)
Revelstoke – 1x/quarter
Niagara – 14 days/year
Foreign Travel – 1x/year (10+ days)

Step Three: Log, Review, Reflect
Daily: 5 minutes of logging before bed. I record mood, activity, nutrition, sleep, and more.
Weekly: I reflect on trends every Sunday.
Monthly: I adjust targets and reset intentions.
Quarterly and Annually: I zoom out—review the arc of my progress, the changes in how I feel, and the goals I'm working toward.

The power isn't just in the numbers. It's in the awareness.

Even a rough record of how you spend your time can reveal what matters most—and what's missing.

Data Visualization (Optional)

Using Excel, I created charts and trend lines that let me track streaks, spot slumps, and celebrate progress. You could use Google Sheets, Notion, or even paper if that suits you better.

An app version would be even more powerful—designed to automate and simplify these functions while keeping the soul of the system intact. That's the dream, and one I still plan to bring to life.

Results: The Data Behind the Discipline

By the time spring arrived in 2025, I wasn't just surviving—I was living the 24HrDay. Every habit I'd tracked, every system I'd designed, every commitment I'd made was in motion. And unlike most wellness philosophies that disappear into abstraction, mine had data. Measurable. Visible. Real.

These five weekly snapshots, taken just before everything changed on April 16th, offer undeniable proof:

1. Fitness & Movement

I was consistently exceeding my weekly goals for movement, calorie burn, and exercise—while maintaining healthy energy, mood, and stress levels. Every day, I was earning it.

2. Effort & Emotional Regulation

Beyond physical health, I tracked my emotional discipline. Effort. Relaxation. Sleep. Mood. I wasn't just showing up—I was present, calm, and aligned.

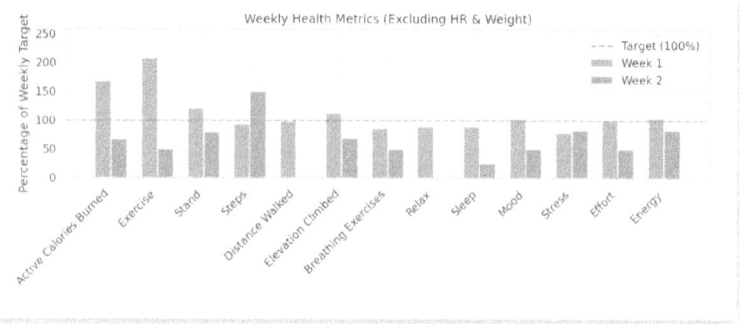

Physical and Mental Health Results - Week 1 and Week 2

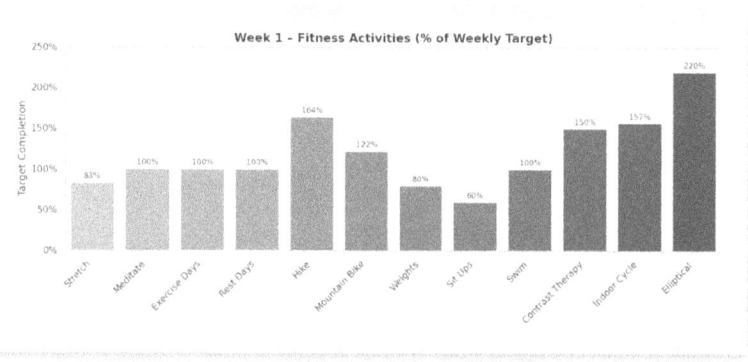

Fitness Activity Results - Week 1 and Week 2

3. Nutrition & Supplement Intake

Protein, probiotics, hydration, medication, vitamins—it was all there. The fuel matched the fire. No guessing. No gaps. Just consistent, high-quality input.

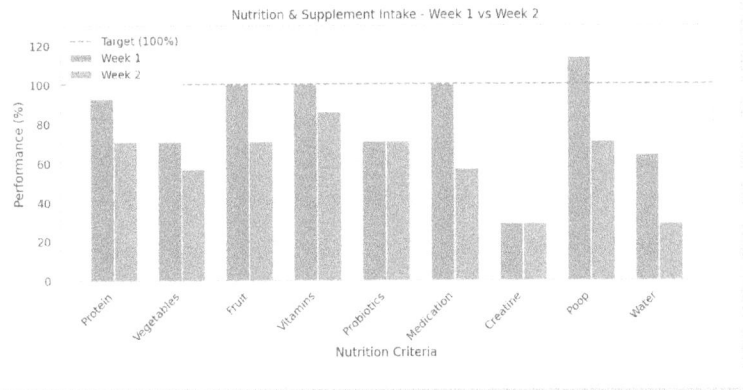

Nutrition Results - Week 1 and Week 2

4. Personal Hygiene

I treated my body like it mattered—because it did. From brushing and flossing to grooming and showering, I honoured the vessel that carried me.

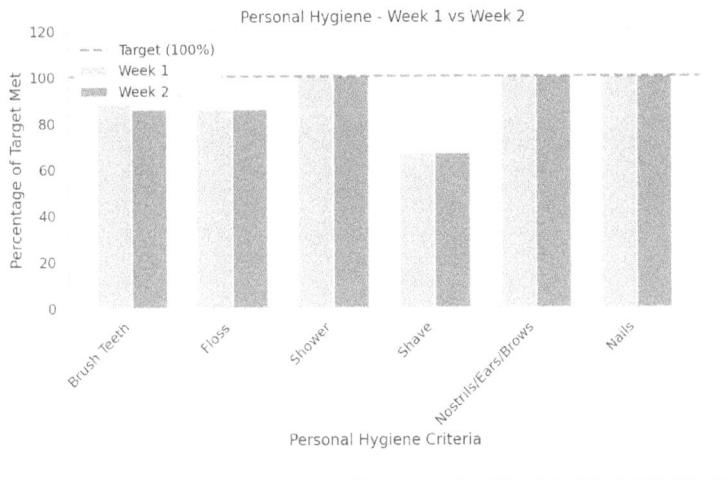

Personal Hygiene Results - Week 1 and Week 2

5. Home & Chores

A tidy home. A clean car. Laundry done. Dishes washed. Even the bed was made most days. These weren't chores—they were affirmations of care, order, and presence.

Home and Auto Chore Results - week 1 and Week 2

These graphs don't tell the whole story—but they tell the truth. I was showing up in every category that mattered to me. And for two solid weeks, I was executing the vision I had created. The system worked. I felt strong, light, proud. The data proved what my spirit already knew: I had climbed my way into the best version of myself.

Then—on April 16th—everything changed.

But that's the next story.

That's *Virtuosity*.

Final Word on Practice

This isn't about perfection. It's about presence.

This isn't about maximizing every second. It's about being intentional with how you live.

Whether you're healing from cancer, managing a chronic condition, or simply seeking a more fulfilling life—this system helps you *see* your life more clearly, and shape it with greater purpose.

APPENDIX B

Dr. Andrea MacNeill Interview - April 28, 2025

This appendix features a full transcript of a candid, wide-ranging interview between me and Dr. Andrea MacNeill, conducted on April 28, 2025. It offers an in-depth look at the surgical approach, expectations, and philosophy behind the cytoreductive surgery and HIPEC procedure that played a pivotal role in my cancer treatment and recovery.

The conversation reveals not only the technical detail of the 14-hour procedure but also highlights Dr. MacNeill's compassionate communication style and the nuances of patient care in a universal healthcare system. For readers navigating serious illness, or those supporting a loved one, this unfiltered conversation can serve as both a source of understanding and empowerment.

Bob - What is the primary goal of cytoreductive surgery, and how is it accomplished?

Dr. MacNeill - This surgery is offered to people whose cancer has spread. So people who have, by definition stage four cancer, typically many, many spots of cancer throughout their abdomen, sometimes hundreds or thousands of individual spots. And the goal is to completely remove all of that. Sometimes people use the word debulking for this kind of surgery. That's wrong. We don't really use that word because that word suggests that you get rid of some, but not all of it. Like you take away the bulk, but there's still something there. Our goal is to get rid of every last nodule of cancer in your abdomen. And when that's done, we add in a heated chemotherapy bath to get rid of any microscopic cancer cells that might be floating around and wanting to regrow. And that is accomplished by any means necessary. So we try to be as organ preserving as possible, but the truth is these cancers are typically so widespread that for most people, this procedure requires taking out multiple organs or structures and stripping the lining of the inside of their abdomen. So it's quite an in-depth, extensive and prolonged procedure.

Bob - You touched on HIPEC, please explain this part of the procedure further.

Dr. MacNeill - It's a chemotherapy cocktail, that is heated up to 42 degrees Celsius and infused into the abdomen once all the cancer is gone and it circulates through a pump. So it's continually infused for 60 or 90 minutes after the cancer is gone. We think this helps improve the durability of the surgery in two ways. One, it's chemotherapy, so it's what we call cytotoxic, meaning it kills cells. Firstly, it's a direct application of chemo on cancer. Two, the heat is also cytotoxic. The heat kills cells. So that combination of heated fluid and toxic chemotherapy basically bursts the cancer cells that might be floating around remaining and potentially regrowing after the procedure.

Bob - Which types of cancer typically require these procedures?

Dr. MacNeill - In B.C. we offer this, for colon and appendix cancers that have spread throughout the abdomen. So that's the peritoneal cavity. We call those peritoneal metastases or a couple of rare cancers that originate in the peritoneum. One is called mesothelioma. That's a rare cancer that most people have only heard of in the lungs related to asbestos exposure,

It can happen in the abdomen as well, typically not related to asbestos. And then there are rare tumours, like rare types of sarcomas that do the same thing. There are studies suggesting some ovarian cancers could benefit from this as well. That's not currently done in BC, but it's done in some places in the world. And there's a lot of work happening, especially in Asia right now on gastric cancer, which is stomach cancer because it tends to spread throughout the abdomen. That's the dominant pattern of spread of gastric cancer. It's not to go to lungs or into your liver, not to go into the organs or the bloodstream. To spread throughout the abdomen, which makes it amenable to this procedure.

Bob - Thank you for the explanation. Please outline the procedures performed during my 14-hour surgery. What parts did you handle and which parts were conducted by Dr. Vasilyeva?

Dr. MacNeill - I'll say up front that it's a team sport. We undertake these procedures together so that we can spell each other off and give one another breaks because it is prolonged, but for the most part, the benefit is that you're operating together with another skilled qualified surgeon. So it takes a hard surgery and makes it much more manageable.

Bob - Please run me through the timeline of what occurred during my surgery.

Dr. MacNeill - We got started about quarter to nine in the morning. The anesthesia time is quite prolonged. They need more than an hour to get you ready. The first thing we did was take out the right colon, the original source of your tumor, the cecum, which is part of the right colon. You had what's called a right heme-colectomy first, and then we took out the omentum. The omentum is a fatty layer that everybody has which hangs down like an apron and cushions your organs. It doesn't really have a function. You don't notice when it's gone, you don't need it. But it is a hotspot for metastatic disease for peritoneal metastases. So it's usually the first place we see people's cancer spread. We always take that out as part of this procedure, even if it's visibly normal, because often there'll be microscopic cancer in it. It is absolutely a lightning rod for this kind of cancer.

You have a greater omentum, which is the big one, and the weirdly titled lesser omentum, which as the name suggests is the smaller one. We removed both of those. You don't know that after. You don't miss them. And then we stripped the diaphragm. In your case you had lots of little nodules of disease on the inside of the right diaphragm, which is the muscle that's going to separate your abdomen from your chest. And so we take that lining off. It's similar to the omentum, you don't normally know when you don't have it. It doesn't normally cause any functional consequences, but it takes an hour to do. It's quite an involved part of the procedure to do that stripping.

It's over some pretty critical structures, big veins. That takes a bit of time. You had nodules along both sides of your abdomen, what we officially call the flanks. So we stripped the flanks. Left diaphragm was fine. We did not have to strip the left diaphragm. We stripped the right lining of the diaphragm, both flanks, and then the pelvis. The pelvis, we stripped the whole lining off the back of the bladder and the sides of the pelvis. You lost most of the lining of the inside of your abdomen. Only your left diaphragm was left untouched. Then we focused on the pelvis. And very commonly that's the site of most concentrated disease. Honestly, just by gravity, people spend most of their time standing up and the metastasis fall to the pelvis. So most people have disease involving their rectum when we do this. And that was the case for you. So, we also removed a portion of the rectum. We took the right colon and a portion of the rectum, so two different sections of the colon.

You also had scattered nodules along the blood supply, what we call the mesentery, which is the blood supply to both the small intestine and the large intestine. That's a long laborious process of either removing what we call excising those nodules, or if they're not even big enough to be removed, we obliterate them with high voltage electricity. We kind of blast the cells and burn them off. The technical term is *electrocoagulation*. We have a very high voltage pen, and for stuff that is just surface like a little tiny dot, too small to be physically plucked off, we literally obliterate it with this pen. So we did that to all of those little nodules. After getting rid of the cancer, then we put the heated chemo in.

Bob - How long did all of this take to this point?

Dr. MacNeill - That took about 11 hours. And then about an hour of chemo. There's some setting up time for that and getting it up to temperature. It runs for an hour once it gets to target. And then there's an evacuation process for the chemo. We thoroughly wash out the abdomen with many litres of saline to get rid of all the chemo. And then we put everything back together. So in your case, after we took out two pieces of bowel we had two new connections to make. The one between the colon and the rectum is a trickier connection. It's a bit complicated. The connection between the small bowel and the colon where the right colon was taken is an easier one to make. These both take a bit of time. Then some drains were added and a few other finishing things. So that takes a couple of hours, about two and a half hours of reconstruction enclosure. And then there's the closing up.

Bob - I'm just curious, is the peritoneum lining stitched too?

Dr. MacNeill - No, it's gone. We stripped it. You no longer have a lining.

Bob - I don't have a peritoneal lining?

Dr. MacNeill - Only on your left diaphragm.

Bob - Does that explain why I'm experiencing some tightness there?

Dr. MacNeill - It could be. Most people don't really notice any functional difference, but yeah, it's part of why you get so scarred after. The nice slippery surfaces are gone.

Bob - Thank you for that detailed description. That was a lot more than I had been told or known about. Were there any complications or was everything as expected?

Dr. MacNeill - No complications, but the one unexpected finding was that there was more cancer there than we had expected based on the laparoscopy you'd had done. And that sometimes happens, we find the laparoscopy usually slightly underestimates because you don't get the same view with a little camera as you do when somebody's wide open. But in your case, you were hiding more in the little nooks and crannies that are not accessible to laparoscopy. So you had more of a disparity between what we were expecting from the laparoscopy and what we found in real life.

We hadn't prepared you mentally for a 14 hour procedure because we were under the impression there was less there. We expected it to be slightly faster, but we have to be prepared for anything when we do these surgeries. That was the unexpected finding for your surgery.

Bob - How do patients generally react in the weeks and months that follow this type of procedure?

Dr. MacNeill - Everybody is different. People experience pain and recovery very differently, which is really interesting to watch. Some people are very debilitated by pain and other people you just wouldn't think we'd done surgery at all. It is a remarkable spectrum of experience. In general, I prepare people to feel like they've been hit by a truck. We're pretty good at managing pain. You have your epidural in and the anaesthetists see you every day. They can keep the pain away, but they can't get rid of that sense of profound fatigue that the patient has just been beaten up, the feeling that somebody has sucked out their soul. The sensation is comparable to feeling like you have been hit by a truck. It's not so much pain as what on earth happened to me. Recovery of energy, vigour and stamina is the longest part of the recovery. And that is what is most common, what is most generalizable. No matter how much pain somebody has or doesn't have, whether they have complications or not, it takes a long time to get your energy back after taking a pummelling on the inside.

Bob - For me, it was about two months until I felt okay again.

Dr. MacNeill - Typically that's as short as it gets. You're on the front end of the recovery curve.

Bob - I remember you telling me it could take three to six months.

Dr. MacNeill - That's more typical, three to six months.

Bob - Now I'm at the six month period.

Dr. MacNeill - And you look like you're two years out. This is well behind you.

Bob - A few months after the surgery, I received a letter saying I had received albumin during the procedure. What is albumin and why was it administered?

Dr. MacNeill - Don't honestly know why they have to send you that letter, but it's a bovine protein. Albumin is derived from cows. It's a protein that we all have in our blood that is a more effective way of replacing somebody's fluid volume than just saline after surgery.

Bob - So it's not that I lost a lot of blood?

Dr. MacNeill - No, not at all. You're attached to your IV and they're just running saline. It's like pure liquid and it's in a litre bag. Albumin is a more concentrated version of that, and it's not pure liquid. It's thicker and it's a part of all of our blood. It's a normal component, but we have a way of manufacturing it from cows in a way that's safe for humans to use. It's just a more effective resuscitation fluid than pure saline. For a long procedure we usually use albumin.

Bob - How long has cytoreductive surgery been practiced and when did HIPEC become available?

Dr. MacNeill - Kind of interesting because in surgical timelines, much like geological timelines, this is a young procedure, which means it was invented in the nineties. It's not that young. But we don't have seismic shifts in practice that often. Like the advent of an entirely new surgical technique for a condition that without it was universally fatal. It was universally fatal before HIPEC was available.

It was a terminal diagnosis, and this is one of the numbers I'll look at for you, but I think before this surgery, maybe nine to 12 months, and certainly five years for anyone that had it. I mean, there's still going to be a spectrum because some people will have one centimetre of disease and some people will have a thousand nodules of disease. So there is still a wide variability in the idea of peritoneal metastases and that plays into survival. But any peritoneal spread would've been universally a terminal diagnosis in probably 12 months would be my guess.

So now with this technique, and importantly with advances in chemotherapy as well, systemic therapy, chemo immunotherapy, different drugs that the medical oncologists have at their disposal, the five-year survival has gone from 5% to over 50%. And the average survival has gone from say, 12 months, something in that range to 44 months. So it's still not curing most people, there's a small proportion of people whose cancer doesn't come back. It's a significant survival gain compared to hopefully it's not coming back.

Bob - Are there any known factors that could increase the likeliness of somebody developing intraperitoneal cancer?

Dr. MacNeill - Not really. It is a feature of some cancers more than others. Gastric cancer, like I mentioned, just the one that most often spreads in this pattern of spreading throughout the peritoneum and nowhere else, but it is also tendency of colon and appendix cancers. I know your next question is about your burst appendix, which is relevant in that the only factor, aside from just the type of cancer and its own inherent biological tendencies that could predispose someone to this type of spread is if their tumour had perforated. So whether that's an appendix cancer or a colon cancer, some people's cancer comes to light when it breaks open. That's the first inkling they have, that they have cancer, they don't have blood in their stools, they don't have any other signs, their cancer bursts. And if your tumour bursts open, then there is a higher likelihood of it spreading throughout the abdomen than if it has been always contained. But I don't think that was your case.

Bob - My appendix burst three years prior to my cancer diagnosis.

Dr. MacNeill - Prior, exactly before you had a cancer. So I doubt that played a role, but nobody will ever know. We will never know that 100%.

Bob - I thought being in the same area three years prior and maybe was related somehow.

Dr. MacNeill - It's a good thought. Yeah. Don't know. Your cancer might have taken a few years to develop, so if there was some sort of early progenitor of your cancer at that time, maybe some cells got out when your appendix burst. I can't rule that out. It's a possibility. Interesting. But it's not the likeliest explanation. This is a relatively common root of spread for colon cancers, but it's an interesting nuance to your case that happened in that timeline.

Bob - Do you have any idea how long I had cancer before it was diagnosed?

Dr. MacNeill - It's very hard to know. We used to think, 20 years ago, that cancers took five to 10 years based on the earliest sequence that was elucidated. It looked like it took 5-10 years. But now we know that there are different pathways from polyp to cancer, and some of them are slower and some a lot faster. It is largely driven by what underlying mutation went awry giving rise to the cancer. Some mutations have a fast track to cancer and typically a more aggressive course of the cancer than others.

Bob - Can you tell that from the biopsy?

Dr. MacNeill - Sometimes, yes. There are certain mutations we know are associated with very aggressive cancers, and as a result, very poor prognosis like BRAF F mutations, which you did not have. We typically can't do this surgery if somebody has a BRAF F mutation. Those are very aggressive, and those cancers develop quite quickly.

Bob - So the timing of this for me, when I was diagnosed, I feel like it was fortunate because I had blood in my stool that was not even related to the cancer. It was related to a hemorrhoid. I feel like I was super lucky. If I had my colonoscopy six months sooner, it might even not have been visible from inside the colon.

Dr. MacNeill - Maybe six months I suspect it would've been there. But if you'd had your colonoscopy 18 months before, two years before, maybe not. Possibly not. Hard to know.

Bob - Maybe 10 months later it might've been too late kind of thing?

Dr. MacNeill - Might have gotten really lucky. Yeah. Don't have a sense for what rate of growth you had. So I agree, we got very lucky.

Bob - What types of complications might patients experience following this type of surgery not related to say the cancer actually coming back? Any other sort of digestive issues related to the surgery?

Dr. MacNeill - Yeah. I mean we try to be very frank with people that this is a major surgery and it has some associated significant risks. There is a risk of dying from this surgery. It is under 2% risk, but some people certainly don't make it through. That would likely be due to what we would consider catastrophic complications like a heart attack or stroke. Typically more in an elderly person, a pulmonary embolus, a blood clot to the lungs. That's something that can be a fatal complication. An aspiration, which is when you vomit into your lungs. So when you're waking up from surgery, you're not conscious yet and kind of protecting your airway the way you normally do. You can vomit and if that goes into the lungs, that can be catastrophic.

And then there are surgical related complications like catastrophic bleeding or infection that can be overwhelming. Those all have the potential to be very serious, even potentially fatal complications. Thankfully that is exceedingly rare, but the risk of major complication is between 15 to 30%. Major being defined as something that needs an intervention, whether that's a re-operation or a drain placed into a pocket of infection or some sort of intervention, it is between 15 and 30% of people who have something like that happen.

Bob - What treatments did patients with peritoneal cancer undergo prior to the advent of HIPEC?

Dr. MacNeill - Just chemo was all we had. We had palliative chemo, and honestly it's not comparable to the chemo we have now. It was primitive palliative chemo. Our chemos now are much better than what people had 20 years ago before HIPEC was available.

Bob - Is this because the chemo is more targeted at the cancer than it was before?

Dr. MacNeill - In general there are more options. There's multiple different cocktails of chemo that are now effective against colon and appendix cancers, whereas there only used to be basically one option and now there are more targeted therapies.

Bob - How much have survival rates improved with the advancements in HIPEC?

Dr. MacNeill - Those are the numbers I gave you earlier. Like 5% to 50% gain.

Bob - Are you able to ballpark the estimated cost in U.S. based on the surgeries, imaging, chemotherapy, wound care etc. I received as part of my entire cancer treatment plan?

Dr. MacNeill - I can't for the whole package of care, but I can compare surgical costs because we have had people pursue this treatment in the U.S. and for the surgery that you had here and the length the hospital stay after that would've been about $200,000 in the U.S. And I mean, I don't get a bill for your stay, but we know the costs I've seen have been about $30,000 for our costs here for a comparable treatment.

I don't know what our chemo's would cost here. Most of them are off patent, meaning they're not super expensive anymore. Drugs are always most expensive when they're new. Then when the patents expire, they become much more affordable.

Many of these have been around long enough that they're not in that super elite, very expensive range anymore. But I expect that they are three to four times more in the U.S.

Bob - I'm so grateful that this happened to me in Canada. I'm very lucky.

Dr. MacNeill - Grateful too that we have robust care here. It's devastating enough to give someone this diagnosis and talk about facing a daunting procedure like this. I don't know how people honestly function in a system where you have to add the possibility of personal bankruptcy that may lead to financial ruin. It's a life changing diagnosis. We are so lucky. I am so grateful to work in a system where I know there are significant out-of-pocket costs and it is still financially devastating for people to get a cancer diagnosis when they can no longer work and they have to be going to repeated appointments and paying for travel and parking and things like that. It adds up, but it is nothing compared to what people face in the U.S.

ABOUT THE AUTHOR

BOB CAIN is a passionate advocate for cancer awareness and a survivor of stage 4 colon cancer. He holds an Honours BA in Neuroscience from Brock University and a diploma in Electronic Engineering Technology from Niagara College—an uncommon blend of scientific insight and technical skill that informs both his writing and his worldview.

A lifelong innovator, Bob is the inventor of a U.S. patent for an early warning device designed to assist individuals with epilepsy—reflecting his deep commitment to improving lives through empathy, design, and purpose.

24HrDay is Bob's first book: a raw, deeply personal chronicle of survival, transformation, and hope. His forthcoming titles, *Virtuosity* and *Warrior*, continue the journey—diving into the art of resilience, the power of purpose, and the pursuit of inner strength.

In addition to his work as an author, Bob is a musician and producer of the original 12-song album *Blue Morning Light*(2017). He is also the founder of **Eco-Train Inc.**, a pioneering Canadian company dedicated to helping the wireless industry transition to a circular economy.

Bob lives in Coquitlam, British Columbia, with his life partner, **D'Arcy Saunders**. Together, they embrace each day with purpose, gratitude, and love. Through 24HrDay, Bob invites others to do the same—by living fully, loving deeply, and holding on to hope, even in the darkest hours.

www.Ingramcontent.com/pod-product-compliance
Lightning Source LLC
Chambersburg PA
CBHW040246010526
44119CB00057B/844